Project CRISS^{SM} for Students

It's a Brain Thing ~ Learning How to Learn!

Project CRISS℠ for Students

It's a Brain Thing ~ Learning How to Learn!

Authors
Lynn T. Havens
Kalispell, Montana

Bonnie J. Valdes
Largo, Florida

Consulting Author
Carol M. Santa, Ph.D.
Kalispell, Montana

Lifelong Learning, Inc.
DBA Project CRISS℠
40 Second Street East, Suite 249
Kalispell, Montana 59901
www.projectcriss.com

Project CRISS^{SM} for Students: It's a Brain Thing ~ Learning How to Learn!

Published by Lifelong Learning, Inc.
40 Second Street East, Suite 249
Kalispell, MT 59901
Phone: 406-758-6440
Fax: 406-758-6444
criss@projectcriss.com
www.projectcriss.com

Project Editor: Dorothy C. Huff

Inspiration® Software was used to create a number of the
graphic organizers as noted throughout the book.
www.inspiration.com

ISBN 0-9746827-0-5

Printed in the United States of America.
08 07 06 05 04 10 9 8 7 6 5 4 3 2 1

DEDICATION

To our parents,

Wilfrid & Helen Dempster
Harlan & Mary Broadie

our first role models, who instilled the love of reading
and learning within us.

To our husbands,

Gary Havens
Jose Valdes

for their continuous support and encouragement.

To our mentor

Dr. Carol Santa

for being a special friend who has shared her wisdom
and given us tremendous guidance.

For

ALL STUDENTS ON THE ROAD TO "LEARNING HOW TO LEARN."

TABLE OF CONTENTS

ILLUSTRATIONS

Cover picture and predator illustrations by
Carol Ackerson and Alice P. Haynes.
Eagle
Tiger
Ladybird Beetle (Ladybug)
North Pacific Giant Octopus
Aplomado Falcon
Saltwater Crocodile
Community Spider
Great Barracuda
Pitcher Plant
Siphonophore
Gray Wolf
Dragonfly
Gray Whale, page 161

Illustrations by
Lynn T. Havens.
Grizzly Bear
Gray Whale, page 166
Diamondback Rattlesnake

Cover Design
Book Layout and Design
by
Fossil Advertising & Design Co.
Kalispell, Montana.
www.fossil2.com

All other illustrations, graphs, and charts
designed, created, or compiled by
Lynn T. Havens and Dorothy C. Huff
unless otherwise noted.

Project CRISS^{SM} for Students
It's a Brain Thing ~ Learning How to Learn!

PREFACE

Project CRISS^{SM} (**CR**eating **I**ndependence through **S**tudent-owned **S**trategies) is a teacher training program designed to help teachers incorporate learning strategies into their regular classroom instruction. Because the project has been so successful, we thought it was time to share our strategies and keys to successful learning directly with students.

Project CRISS^{SM} for Students: It's a Brain Thing ~ Learning How to Learn! contains lots of ideas which will help you learn from the reading materials used in all of your classes. As you try out the various strategies, we hope you will identify those that work best for you. Not all people learn the same way, and you will not necessarily be using the same strategies in all of your classes. For example, you may find the *Problem Solving Guide* helpful in your mathematics class, while the strategy *Power Notes* works better when you want to organize for writing. As you learn and practice each strategy, we want you to ask yourself "Does this strategy help me learn?" and "How can I use this strategy in my other classes?"

Meet the Chapter 1 KEY TO LEARNING
and Strategy "At a Glance"

AUTHOR'S CRAFT

Be a *reading detective*.

bold

color

MAIN
IDEAS

italics

DETAILS

visuals

HEADINGS
Sub-headings

TWO-COLUMN NOTES	
Feature	**Use**
Chapter Title	Provides the topic of the terminator chapter
Map	Shows where the animal lives

Introduction and KEY TO LEARNING No. 1– Author's Craft

KEY TO LEARNING

Purpose

- **Process:** To learn the purpose of this class, to become familiar with the course materials used in this class, to learn strategies for discovering the KEY TO LEARNING No. 1–Author's Craft, and to be able to apply these strategies in other classes.

CRISS^{SM} Learning Plan (A-1)

Prepare: *Questions*
Be Involved: *Author's Craft*
Organize: *Two-Column Notes (Feature–Use)*
Apply: *Author's Craft Implementation*

Implementation

PREPARE: *What's this class about? What do I already know?*

- Turn to page xvii and read the part of this book called "Preface."

- In the space below, write one sentence, in your own words, that says what you think you are going to learn in this class.

_____

_____

- In the following chart, list the strategies you currently use to study and learn information for each type of class.

STUDY STRATEGIES I USE NOW

Class: _____ Mathematics _____	Class: _____ English _____
Class: _____ Social Studies _____	**Class: _____ Science _____**

BE INVOLVED: *KEY TO LEARNING (A-2) No. 1—Author's Craft with Project CRISS^SM for Students*

- Take a quick tour of this book to discover how the authors organized the information. All authors write with a message in mind, but not all authors present their ideas in the same way. One thing a reader needs to do to be successful is to figure out how the material is organized. We call this organization the "Author's Craft."

- As you do your whole book survey, use the following chart. Write down, in the left-hand column, features you notice and, in the right-hand column, how you can use them and how you think they can help you learn. Use an additional sheet of paper if needed.

Feature	How I can use it? How it will help me learn?
1. Preface	1. The Preface tells me what I will be learning and that I need to apply the strategies I learn to all my classes.
2.	2.

ORGANIZE: *Two-Column Notes (Feature-Use)*

- Your teacher will help you organize the class information so all the features that occur consistently within each *chapter* will be together and all the features that deal with the *whole book* will be together.

- To make sure you recorded the important features for the *chapters* and for the *whole book*, read through the two "Did you discover the following?" sections with your teacher.

Project CRISS[SM] *for Students* Chapter Organization

Did you discover the following?

Meet the Strategies "At a Glance." Opposite the first page of each chapter, you will find a quick reference to strategies and KEYS TO LEARNING in a graphic format. You will also find these strategies and a few more in the Appendices at the end of this book.

Purpose. Each chapter begins with a purpose statement. In most chapters, you will see both a "Process" and a "Content" purpose. The Process purpose will include the names of the strategies to be introduced in that chapter. The Content purpose will let you know what types of information you need to pay attention to as you read *Tough Terminators*.

CRISS[SM] ***Learning Plan (A-1).*** Below the Purpose, you will find a brief overview of the CRISS[SM] Learning Plan you will use to learn the information in the chapter or in one of the chapters of *Tough Terminators*.

Implementation. This section directs your learning through the four steps in the CRISS[SM] Learning Plan:

1. **How to PREPARE for reading.** This will show you strategies for bringing out your background knowledge on the topic and for setting a purpose for reading and learning.
2. **How to BE INVOLVED during reading.** These strategies will help you pay attention to and focus on the most important information in the selection.

3. **How to <u>ORGANIZE</u> the information you learned.** Once you have actively read the selection, you need to organize the information into notes which you can study and learn.

4. **How to <u>APPLY</u> the information you organized.** The strategies used after you have organized the information into notes will help you study, apply, and learn for long-term retention.

Check Your Understanding. This section will help you identify if you have learned the information about a KEY TO LEARNING or about one of the predators in *Tough Terminators* (<u>MULTIPLE CHOICE</u> and <u>WRITING ITEM</u>) and if the strategies you used worked for you (<u>REFLECTION</u>).

Apply This to Other Classes. This is probably the most important part of each chapter. If you have truly learned the strategies, you will be able to see how they will help you learn in another subject. This gives you a chance to plan strategy use in other classes.

Project CRISS^{SM} *for Students* Whole Book Organization

Did you discover the following?

KEYS TO LEARNING. (A-2) Mixed in with the chapters dealing with the animals in *Tough Terminators* are four chapters dealing with the five *KEYS TO LEARNING.* These are really important ingredients for learning. Although you will not be introduced to all of them at the beginning of this book, you will see that you are already using all of them in this first chapter.

1. <u>AUTHOR'S CRAFT</u>. Authors write to convey a message. Each author has his or her own style. To more easily read and understand the information from any written piece (textbook, magazine, novel, comic book), we need to determine the Author's Craft or way of writing.

2. <u>BACKGROUND KNOWLEDGE</u>. Scientists tell us we learn and remember new information by relating it to what we already know. So, as you go through the four steps of the CRISS^{SM} Learning Plan, always try to make connections to what you know or do.

3. <u>PURPOSE SETTING</u>. To be successful, you need to have a purpose for reading and learning. Usually, your teacher will tell you the purpose, but sometimes you will have to figure it out using the author's clues and your own background knowledge.

4. <u>**ACTIVE LEARNING**</u>. You absolutely cannot learn something if you are not paying attention. When you "actively" involve yourself in learning, you think about the information you read and try to make sense of it. Three types of strategies which will help you pay attention are (1) DISCUSSING, (2) WRITING, and (3) ORGANIZING.

5. <u>**METACOGNITION**</u>. "Metacognition" looks and sounds important—and it is! It means that during the Learning Plan you continually monitor your learning. Here are some questions you can use to check yourself: "Do I know the purpose for reading?" "Does this make sense?" "Is this strategy working for me?" If you have to answer "No," then you need a plan to get yourself back on track. Metacognition consists of these two parts: (1) knowing when learning is happening in your head and (2) knowing what to do if it is not.

Appendices: Strategies Reference. Starting on page 177 are several Appendices. In this section, we group the learning strategies into categories, such as "Organizing Strategies," "Writing Strategies," and "Vocabulary Strategies." For each strategy, we provide a quick overview.

When each strategy is introduced in this book, we give the Appendix listing. For example, "(A-2)" after "KEY TO LEARNING" below lets you know to look in Appendix <u>A</u>, the <u>second</u> illustration. The Appendices also include a few additional strategies you might like to try.

• Now, your teacher will assign several of the features to you and your partner. Create a poster to explain these features.

<u>APPLY</u>: *KEY TO LEARNING (A-2) No. 1—Author's Craft with Tough Terminators*

• To make sure you understand how to determine the Author's Craft or style, you will now evaluate the *Tough Terminators* book using the process you just learned in evaluating this book.

• In the chart on the following page, list features and how you can use them.

TWO-COLUMN NOTES (FEATURE–USE)
The Author's Craft for *TOUGH TERMINATORS*

Feature	How I can use it? How it will help me learn?
<u>Whole Book</u>: <u>Chapter</u>:	

- Create two posters to display in your classroom, one which explains the whole book features and one which explains the chapter features.

Check Your Understanding

MULTIPLE CHOICE: *(Circle the letter of the correct response.)* According to the authors, the five KEYS TO LEARNING are really important ingredients to learning. In addition to the Author's Craft, what do the authors list as the other FOUR Keys?
  A. Prepare, Be Involved, Organize, and Apply
  B. Preface, Introduction, Chapters, and Strategy Reference
  C. Purpose, Strategies At a Glance, Implementation, and Check Your Understanding
  D. Background Knowledge, Purpose Setting, Active Learning, and Metacognition

WRITING ITEM: Why do you think it is important to know the Author's Craft? In your response, include three ways this knowledge could help you learn.

_____

_____

_____

_____

_____

_____

_____

_____

REFLECTION
- Talk about how the strategy of Two-Column Notes and the KEY TO LEARNING No. 1—Author's Craft helped you understand and remember the styles in which the authors of this book and the author of *Tough Terminators* wrote.

- What could you have done to be more successful with your learning?

_____

_____

_____

_____

Apply This to Other Classes

- Think about how you can apply the learning strategy of Two-Column Notes and the KEY TO LEARNING No. 1—Author's Craft to your other classes. Record your thoughts below.

_____

_____

_____

_____

- Remember to save samples of successful applications to share with the class and to place in your folder.

Meet the Chapter 2 KEYS TO LEARNING
"At a Glance"

BACKGROUND KNOWLEDGE

PURPOSE SETTING

✓ What is the topic?

✓ What do I need to know?

✓ Why is it important?

DISCUSSION

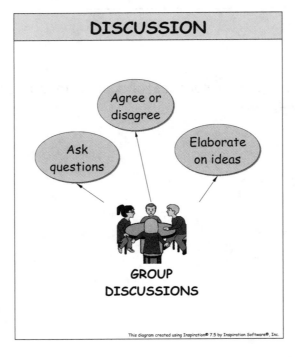

KEY TO LEARNING No. 2– Background Knowledge
KEY TO LEARNING No. 3– Purpose Setting
Plus Discussion

Purpose

- **Process:** To become familiar with the KEY TO LEARNING No. 2–Background Knowledge and KEY TO LEARNING No. 3–Purpose Setting, to understand how the process of "Discussion" helps in the learning process, and to be able to apply these concepts in other classes.

CRISS^{SM} Learning Plan

Prepare: *Background Knowledge*
Be Involved: *Background Knowledge and Purpose Setting*
Organize: *Discussion*
Apply: *Classroom Posters*

Implementation

PREPARE: *How does* BACKGROUND KNOWLEDGE *(A-2) work* BEFORE *reading?*

- Your teacher will read a selection to you without bringing out your background knowledge. Listen carefully and, in the space provided below, write down any notes that might help you figure out the meaning.

_____

_____

_____

- Your teacher will read the selection again after bringing out your background knowledge on the topic. Does the selection make more sense this time? Why?

_____

_____

_____

BE INVOLVED 1: *How does* BACKGROUND KNOWLEDGE *(A-2) impact comprehension* DURING *reading?*

- Read the background knowledge selection your teacher hands out to you, then explain the content of what you read to a partner who was given a different selection.

- What did you discover about background knowledge while you read?

_____

_____

_____

BE INVOLVED 2: *How does* PURPOSE SETTING *(A-2) impact* comprehension DURING *reading?*

- Your teacher is going to give you a purpose for reading the following selection, "After School," and ask you to underline or highlight information which would be important to your purpose for reading.

- Write your purpose here: _____
  Discuss with your partner or group the types of information you should be looking for and list them below.

  _____

  _____

  _____

- In your group, read one paragraph at a time and discuss whether there is any information in that section which would be important for your purpose. If so, underline or highlight it. Make sure your group can justify why you selected that material.

AFTER SCHOOL

School was out. They ran to Jamie's car, which was always unlocked, and jumped in. Jamie slammed the door and noticed that her shoulder still ached when she did that pulling motion. Jacob started his usual search for food, but only came up with an empty pack of cigarettes.

"Not mine," Jamie said, "I'll never smoke. It is so disgusting! It's probably from my brother. He borrowed my car yesterday."

Jacob wondered why, if she didn't smoke, she always had such a bad cough. Although, he guessed she'd had that cough since second grade when he first met her, and he was sure she didn't smoke then.

Jamie carefully pulled out of the student parking lot, while Jacob opened the glove compartment looking for gum. "Hey, what's this?" he asked holding up a traffic ticket.

"Oh, I almost forgot," moaned Jamie. "I got it for going too fast down Main Street. I've got to go pay for it before my parents find out." Jamie coughed a few times as she pulled into the line up at the first stop sign leaving school. "I can't believe how bad your cough sounds." Jacob said, "Have you gone to the doctor?"

"No, I think it's just allergies, because my eyes run, and I get all wheezie—especially in the spring."

Continued ➔

At last she reached the intersection. On her right was Will from her English class. He was driving his dad's old Dodge truck. She waved at him and pulled on through. *(Note: Will had the right-of-way.)*

- In the activity you just did, your teacher gave you the purpose for marking information. In many classes, the teacher will give you the purpose for reading. For example, your teacher might say, "As you read Chapter 4, make sure you learn the four contributions Benjamin Franklin made to our current-day lives." If your teacher does not give you a specific purpose for learning, what can you do? Go through one of your current textbooks and see if the author gives you any help on determining the purpose. List the features below.

Textbook: _____

Features: _____

_____

_____

_____

ORGANIZE: *Discussion (A-2)*

- For one minute, write the most important ideas you learned about the KEYS TO LEARNING No. 2—Background Knowledge and No. 3—Purpose Setting.

_____

_____

_____

_____

_____

_____

- After discussing the Keys with your partner or group, write for another minute on the most important ideas you learned about the KEYS TO LEARNING No. 2–Background Knowledge and No. 3–Purpose Setting.

_____

_____

_____

_____

_____

_____

- In what ways did discussing the ideas in this chapter before writing help you write the previous response?

_____

_____

_____

_____

_____

_____

APPLY: *Create Classroom Posters*

- While doing the activities in this chapter, you discovered the importance of the KEYS TO LEARNING No. 2–Background Knowledge and No. 3–Purpose Setting and the process of "Discussion." Now, your teacher will divide you into groups, and your task will be to make a poster for your classroom which will remind you (1) what the Key or process is, (2) why it is important, and (3) how you can use it to help you learn.

Check Your Understanding

MULTIPLE CHOICE: *(Circle the letter of the correct response.)* With which of the following statements would the authors MOST LIKELY AGREE?

    A. Background knowledge does not have much to do with the way we understand information.

    B. Background knowledge is usually provided by the author.

    C. Background knowledge determines how we understand information.

    D. Background knowledge is important for washing clothes.

WRITING ITEM: *(NOTE: Pick just <u>one</u> of the three numbered items to write about.)* Why do you think it is important to (1) bring out your background knowledge before you read (do a lab, listen to a lecture, etc.), (2) know the purpose for learning before you start to read (do a lab, listen to a lecture, etc.), or (3) discuss ideas from your reading (lecture, field trip, lab, etc.) ? In your response, refer to experiences you have had in this class or in other classes.

_____

_____

_____

_____

_____

_____

_____

REFLECTION

- Talk about how the KEYS TO LEARNING No. 2—Background Knowledge and No. 3—Purpose Setting and the process of "Discussion" helped you understand and remember the selections used and the information presented in this chapter.

• What could you have done to be more successful with your learning?

_____

_____

_____

_____

_____

Apply This to Other Classes

• Think about how you can apply the two KEYS TO LEARNING No. 2–Background Knowledge and No. 3–Purpose Setting and the process of "Discussion" to your other classes. Record your thoughts below.

_____

_____

_____

_____

_____

• Remember to save samples of successful applications to share with the class and to place in your folder.

Meet the Chapter 3 Strategies "At a Glance"

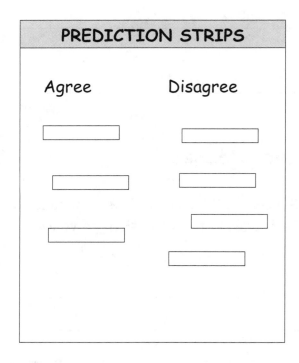

PREDICTION STRIPS

Agree   Disagree

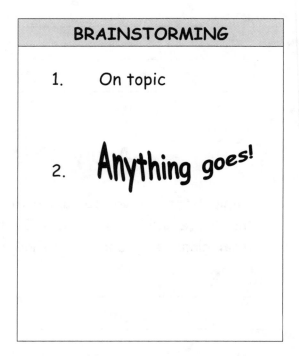

BRAINSTORMING

1. On topic

2. Anything goes!

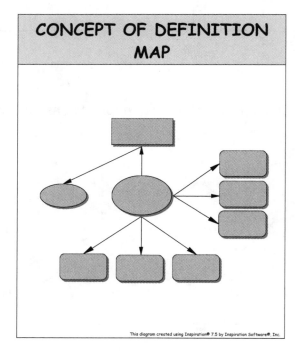

CONCEPT OF DEFINITION MAP

This diagram created using Inspiration® 7.5 by Inspiration Software®, Inc.

CHAPTER 3

About Predators

Purpose

- **Process:** To become familiar with the strategies of Brainstorming, Concept of Definition Map, and Summarization, and to be able to apply these strategies in other classes.

- **Content:** To understand why predators are essential to life on Earth.

CRISS℠ Learning Plan

Prepare: *Prediction Strips and Brainstorming*
Be Involved: *Teacher Read-Aloud*
Organize: *Concept of Definition Map*
Apply: *Summarization*

Implementation

PREPARE 1: *Prediction Strips* (the whole *Tough Terminators* book)

- With a partner, look at the strips of paper your teacher gives you which have statements about each of the twelve predators you will study in *Tough Terminators*. Talk with your partner to determine whether you both AGREE or DISAGREE with each of the statements. Sort the strips into an "agree" and a "disagree" pile. (NOTE: Some of the statements will be pretty difficult, so you may have to make an "educated" guess.)

- When you are done sorting all the strips, your teacher will determine with which statements the majority of class members AGREES and with which statements the majority DISAGREES. Later, as you read about each predator, you will check to see if your class was correct to agree or disagree with the statements.

PREPARE 2: *Brainstorming* ("About Predators")

- To determine your background knowledge about predators, your teacher will have the class brainstorm ideas. If you are not positive about a piece of information, ask your teacher to put a question mark after the item.

BE INVOLVED: *Read-Aloud*

- Silently read along as your teacher reads aloud the "About Predators" selection, pages 4 and 5 of the *Tough Terminators* book. Listen for information which verifies or disproves the information you brainstormed.

ORGANIZE: *Concept of Definition Map (E-3)*

- Your teacher will model how to use the Concept of Definition Map with a few concepts or vocabulary terms.

- Create a Concept of Definition Map for "predator" in the space provided below. You may add more boxes to the graphic if you like. For "examples," record animals which are NOT in the *Tough Terminators* book.

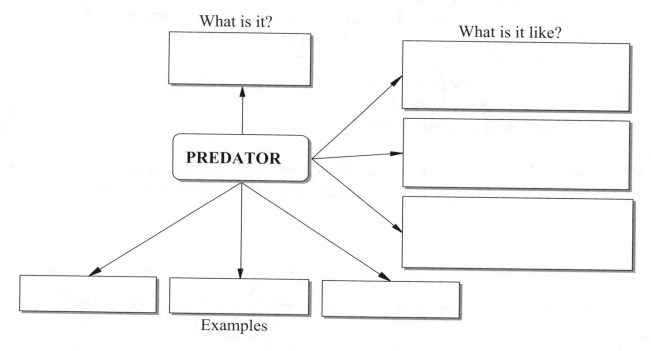

This diagram was created using Inspiration® 7.5 by Inspiration Software®, Inc.

APPLY: *Summarization (D-7)*

- Your teacher will model how to write a summary or definition based on the information in a Concept of Definition Map.

- Using the information in your Concept of Definition Map, write a definition for "predator" in the following space.

_____

_____

_____

_____

_____

_____

Check Your Understanding

MULTIPLE CHOICE: *(Circle the letter of the correct response.)* The author says there are several reasons why people don't always appreciate predators. With which of the following statements would the author MOST LIKELY DISAGREE?
   A. People are afraid of predators.
   B. Predators compete with people for food.
   C. Predators spread diseases.
   D. People don't understand predators very well.

WRITING ITEM: According to the author, predators are essential to life on Earth. Use details and information from the article to support this conclusion.

_____

_____

_____

_____

_____

_____

_____

REFLECTION

- Talk about how the strategies of Brainstorming, Concept of Definition Map, and Summarization helped you to understand and remember the information in the selection on predators.

- What could you have done to be more successful with your learning?

_____

_____

_____

_____

Apply This to Other Classes

- Think about how you can apply these learning strategies to your other classes and record your thoughts below.

_____

_____

_____

_____

_____

- Remember to save samples of successful applications to share with the class and to place in your folder.

Meet the Chapter 4 KEY TO LEARNING and Strategies "At a Glance"

ACTIVE LEARNING

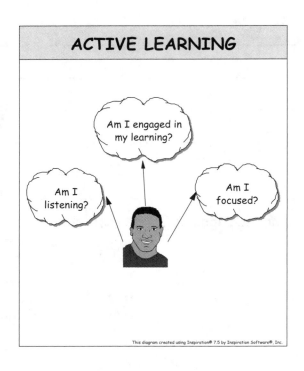

Am I engaged in my learning?

Am I listening?

Am I focused?

This diagram created using Inspiration® 7.5 by Inspiration Software®, Inc.

POWER THINKING

1. Main Idea

2. Support or detail of a Power 1

3. Support or detail of a Power 2

POWER NOTES

1. Animals
   2. Dog
   3. Cairn Terrier
   3. Golden Retriever
   2. Cat
   3. Siamese
   3. Tabby

PATTERN PUZZLES

Use words,
  phrases,
    or sentences.

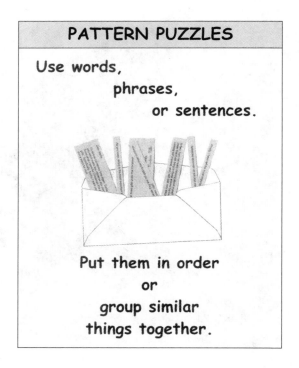

Put them in order
or
group similar
things together.

KEY TO LEARNING No. 4–
Active Learning
Through Power Thinking
and Pattern Puzzles

Purpose

- **Process:** To become familiar with the KEY TO LEARNING No. 4–Active Learning and the strategies Power Thinking, Power Notes, and Pattern Puzzle, and to be able to apply them in other classes.

CRISS^{SM} Learning Plan

Prepare: *Active Learning Through Power Thinking*

Be Involved: *Active Learning Through Power Thinking as You Read*

Organize: *Active Learning Through Power Notes*

Apply: *Active Learning Through Pattern Puzzles*

Implementation

PREPARE: *Active Learning (A-2) Through Power Thinking (A-5)*

- **Active Learning.** In order for you to learn and remember information from reading or listening, you need to be purposefully engaged. You can't just sit back passively and hope the information will stick in your head. Our brains don't work that way. You need to do something with the words you read or hear. Learning will happen when you actively process the information by transforming it into a variety of organizing strategies and by writing and talking.

- Your teacher will introduce you to Power Thinking, a strategy which will help you stay *actively involved* while you read and learn.

- Complete the following Power schemes with your teacher:

1. Furniture	1. Fruit	1. _____
2. Table	2. _____	2. Shorts
2. _____	2. _____	2. T-shirt

- -

- Complete the following Power schemes by yourself:

1. United States
   2. Florida
      3. Tallahassee
  2.
   3.

1. Musical Groups
   2.
   2.
     3.
      4.

BE INVOLVED: *Active Learning (A-2) Through Power Thinking (A-5) as You Read*

• Reading with Powers on your mind can be a good way to get ready for note taking and a good way to stay *actively involved*. Think about each sentence as you read it and how it relates to the other sentences in the paragraph.

• If a text is "considerate," that is, if it is written in a consistent and well-organized way, the Power structure can be figured out. Paragraph 1 and Paragraph 2, which follow, are from a Montana history textbook. Before each sentence in Paragraph 1, we have placed the Power number it represents.

Example: From *A History of Montana* by Susan Dailey

Paragraph 1: (1) The men who became fur trappers were also known as mountain men. **(2)** They had certain characteristics that made them different from the average man of that time. **(3)** They were mostly young men looking for adventure. **(3)** They were very independent and did not like having other people telling them what to do. **(3)** They liked solitude, preferring to be alone rather than in the company of other people. **(3)** They liked seeing new territory that no other white man had seen before. **(3)** They preferred living in nature to the comforts of civilization.

• Using the following paragraph, place the appropriate Power numbers in front of each sentence.

Paragraph 2: ( ) Indians were a big part of the trapper's life. **( )** Some of the tribes were hostile. **( )** The Blackfeet, for example, resented the trappers taking the furs in their territory and did not want the trappers supplying their enemies with guns. **( )** It is thought that at least one trapper was killed by Indians every ten days. **( )** Many tribes, however, such as the Crow and the Flathead, were friendly to the trappers and were eager to trade and socialize with them. **( )** Often, the trappers married Indian women and then lived with a tribe, especially during the winter when the weather was too cold and snowy to trap or to travel.

• **NOTE:** Most often, authors put the Power 1 sentence at the beginning of a paragraph. Look for it there first. Sometimes, though, the Power 1 sentence is the last sentence of the paragraph and some authors even leave it out of a paragraph–it is implied. Look at the following four examples.

1. MAIN IDEA AT THE BEGINNING

(1) *My dog Corky is really energetic.* **(2)** When I wake him up in the morning, he leaps off his pillow and jumps up and down until I put him out. **(2)** Outside, he runs from one end of our yard to the other until I convince him to come in and eat breakfast. **(2)** After breakfast, he wants to play catch. **(2)** Finally, my arm gives out and, when he realizes I am done playing, he chases his tail around for a while, then dashes upstairs to play with another member of the family.

2. MAIN IDEA IN THE MIDDLE

(2) When I wake Corky up in the morning, he leaps off his pillow and jumps up and down until I put him out. **(2)** Outside, he runs from one end of our yard to the other until I convince him to come in and eat breakfast. **(1)** *My dog Corky is really energetic.* **(2)** After breakfast, he wants to play catch. **(2)** Finally, my arm gives out and, when he realizes I am done playing, he chases his tail around for a while, then dashes upstairs to play with another member of the family.

3. MAIN IDEA AT THE END

(2) When I wake Corky up in the morning, he leaps off his pillow and jumps up and down until I put him out. **(2)** Outside, he runs from one end of our yard to the other until I convince him to come in and eat breakfast. **(2)** After breakfast, he wants to play catch. **(2)** Finally, my arm gives out and, when he realizes I am done playing, he chases his tail around for a while, then dashes upstairs to play with another member of the family. **(1)** *My dog Corky is really energetic.*

4. MAIN IDEA IMPLIED

(2) When I wake Corky up in the morning, he leaps off his pillow and jumps up and down until I put him out. **(2)** Outside, he runs from one end of our yard to the other until I convince him to come in and eat breakfast. **(2)** After breakfast, he wants to play catch. **(2)** Finally, my arm gives out and, when he realizes I am done playing, he chases his tail around for a while, then dashes upstairs to play with another member of the family.

POWER NOTES FOR ALL FOUR PARAGRAPHS

1. Corky is energetic
   2. a.m. - leaps off pillow
   2. jumps up and down
   2. runs around yard
   2. plays catch
   2. chases tail
   2. bugs family members to play

- With a partner, look at one of your textbooks from another class. Start at the beginning of a chapter. Look at the chapter title, headings, and subheadings. Do they relate to each other as Powers? _____

- Your teacher will show you how to label the sentences without writing in your text. Work through the first few paragraphs (continue until you get to the end of the first sub-section unless your teacher tells you otherwise) and label each of the sentences as a Power 1, 2, 3, or 4 (or higher if necessary). If appropriate, label the headings, too.

- By carefully reading and evaluating each sentence in a paragraph, you are becoming an active reader. This means you are paying attention to what the words mean and how the ideas the author writes about fit together. In the space provided below, compare how you normally read to how you read while keeping Powers in mind.

_____

_____

_____

_____

_____

ORGANIZE: *Active Learning (A-2) Through Power Notes (A-5)*

• Look again at the mountain men paragraph.

> ***Paragraph 1:*** **(1)** The men who became fur trappers were also known as mountain men. **(2)** They had certain characteristics that made them different from the average man of that time. **(3)** They were mostly young men looking for adventure. **(3)** They were very independent and did not like having other people telling them what to do. **(3)** They liked solitude, preferring to be alone rather than in the company of other people. **(3)** They liked seeing new territory that no other white man had seen before. **(3)** They preferred living in nature to the comforts of civilization.

• If we were to put the information from this paragraph into Power Notes, it would look like this:

   1. Mountain men were fur traders
      2. Traits making them different from others
         3. Adventurous
         3. Independent
         3. Liked being alone
         3. Liked seeing new parts of the country
         3. Preferred wilderness to civilization

• Write out the Power Notes for Paragraph 2 in the space below it on the following page. *(NOTE: Some sentences—such as the third—contain more than one Power entry. Often sentences with "and" or "but" will have two or more pieces of information.)*

Paragraph 2: **(1)** Indians were a big part of the trapper's life. **(2)** Some of the tribes were hostile. **(3)** The Blackfeet, for example, resented the trappers taking the furs in their territory and did not want the trappers supplying their enemies with guns. **(3)** It is thought that at least one trapper was killed by Indians every ten days. **(2)** Many tribes, however, such as the Crow and the Flathead, were friendly to the trappers and were eager to trade and socialize with them. **(3)** Often the trappers married Indian women and then lived with a tribe, especially during the winter when the weather was too cold and snowy to trap or to travel.

Power Notes for Paragraph 2:

APPLY: *Active Learning (A-2) Through Pattern Puzzles (A-4)*

- Pattern Puzzles provide another way for you to stay *actively involved* with your learning. Your teacher will explain to you what a Pattern Puzzle is and model how to put one together.

- With a partner, arrange the sentences your teacher gives to you into a paragraph that makes sense. Remember to use your background knowledge, Powers, and the Author's Craft.

- Now, you and a partner are going to create your own Pattern Puzzles using your mathematics textbook. Go to the chapter you are working on right now or one you have already completed. Find an example problem and solution you have studied, one which is challenging, because your partner is the one who has to solve it! You and your partner should use different examples and use the following procedure.

Procedure for Creating a Mathematics Pattern Puzzle

1. Count the number of steps the author has used. (Remember to count the problem itself as one step.)
2. Cut or tear a piece of paper into enough strips for each step. Mix up the order of the strips before writing on them, so your partner cannot solve the problem by just fitting the strips together!
3. Write the problem on one of the strips, the answer on another strip, and each step of the solution process on separate strips.
4. Mix up the strips and give them to your partner to put in the correct order.
5. When you and your partner are done, each of you will explain your solution. Your partner will evaluate if your solution is right. *Remember*, there may be more than one way to solve the problem, even if the textbook author shows only one way.

Check Your Understanding

MULTIPLE CHOICE: Select the item which would be the best Power 3 to complete the following Power Notes.

1. Food

2. Vegetable 　　　　 2. Fruit 　　　　 2. Meat
　 3. Spinach 　　　　　 3. Apple 　　　　 3. ???

A. Bread
B. Beef
C. Pasta
D. Sloppy Joes

WRITING ITEM: Defend or refute the following statement. *When I use Power Thinking and Pattern Puzzles, I am involved in Active Learning.* In your response, refer to the activities you did in this chapter.

_____

_____

_____

_____

Continue ➡

_____

_____

_____

_____

REFLECTION

- Talk about how the KEY TO LEARNING No. 4–Active Learning and the strategies Power Thinking, Power Notes, and Pattern Puzzles helped you understand and remember the selections used and the information presented in this chapter.

- What could you have done to be more successful with your learning?

_____

_____

_____

_____

Apply This to Other Classes

- Think about how you can apply the KEY TO LEARNING and strategies in this chapter to your other classes. Record your thoughts below.

_____

_____

_____

_____

- Remember to save samples of successful applications to share with the class and to place in your folder.

 No. 1

 No. 2

 No. 3

 No. 4

Meet the Chapter 5 Strategies "At a Glance"

K-W-L

K	W	L
What we <u>Know</u>	What we <u>Want to learn</u>	What we <u>Learned</u>

K-W-L PLUS

Organize *(Power Map)*

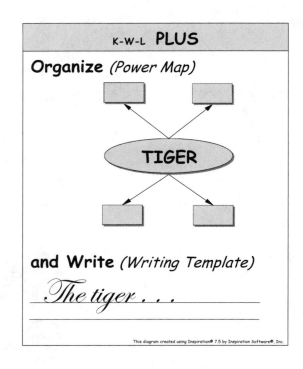

and Write *(Writing Template)*

The tiger . . .

POWER MAP

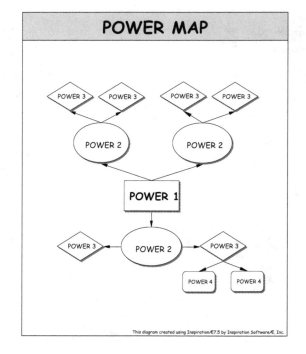

WRITING TEMPLATES

Tigers are interesting wild cats. First . . . . Next . . . . Finally . . . .

Tiger

Purpose

- **Process:** To become familiar with the strategies K-W-L, K-W-L Plus, Power Mapping, and Writing Templates and to be able to apply these strategies in other classes.

- **Content:** To determine why the tiger is considered a skilled hunter.

CRISS^{SM} Learning Plan

Prepare: *K-W-L*
Be Involved: *K-W-L*
Organize: *K-W-L Plus*, *Power Map*
Apply: *K-W-L Plus*, *Writing Template*

Implementation

PREPARE: *K and W of K-W-L (A-3)*

- On the following chart, fill in your responses to the first two questions.

What do you **K**NOW about tigers?	**W**HAT curiosities do you have about tigers?	What have you **L**EARNED about tigers?

Categories of information (Power 2s):

- Looking at the Power 3 information in the first two columns, determine Power 2 categories for the Power 1 topic of "tigers." Write these in the bottom box of the K-W-L Chart.

<u>BE INVOLVED</u>: *L of K-W-L (A-3)*

· Read "Tough Terminator #1, Tiger" and write in the "L" column the new information you learned.

· Also, as you read, look for details which verify or disprove the information you recorded in the "K" column. Put a "✔" by the information which is verified, draw a line through information which was incorrect, and place a "?" by the information that needs further research.

· Look at your categories at the bottom of your K-W-L chart and add to or change them based on the information you recorded in the "L"column.

<u>ORGANIZE</u>: *K-W-L <u>Plus</u> (A-3) Part 1, Power Map (C-3)*

· Reorganize the information from your K-W-L chart into a Power Map similar to the one below. Feel free to add or take away a Power 2 category. List your Power 3 information under the appropriate category.

2. category _____   2. category _____

1. Tiger

2. category _____   2. category _____

APPLY: *K-W-L Plus (A-3) Part 2, Writing Template Summary (D-8)*

- Look at your Power Map and determine the order in which you wish to present the information in your written summary.

- Working with your partner, write your summary in the space provided using the following Writing Template:

Tigers are interesting wild cats. First, they . . . . Next . . . . Finally . . . . In conclusion . . . .

_____

_____

_____

_____

_____

_____

_____

Check Your Understanding

MULTIPLE CHOICE: *(Circle the letter of the correct response.)* Read this sentence from the tiger selection.

"In the back of their eyes is a mirror-like layer called the tapetum that helps tigers—and other nocturnal animals—see in the dark."

What does the word "nocturnal" mean?
- A. large
- B. intelligent
- C. active at night
- D. visually sharp

WRITING ITEM: Summarize why the tiger is described as a skilled hunter. Use details and information from the selection to support your answer.

_____

_____

_____

_____

_____

_____

_____

REFLECTION

• Talk about how the strategies of K-W-L, K-W-L Plus, Power Maps, and Writing Template helped you to understand and remember the information in the selection on the tiger.

• What could you have done to be more successful with your learning?

_____

_____

_____

_____

Apply This to Other Classes

- Think about how you can apply these learning strategies to your other classes and record your thoughts below.

_____

_____

_____

_____

- Remember to save samples of successful applications to share with the class and to place in your folder.

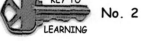 No. 1

 No. 2

 No. 3

KEY TO LEARNING No. 4

Meet the Chapter 6 Strategies "At a Glance"

MIND STREAMING

Start with a topic, then . . .

☞ You talk for 1 minute

switch

Your partner talks ☜ for 1 minute

SELECTIVE UNDERLINING AND HIGHLIGHTING

UNDERLINE
<u>KEY</u> <u>WORDS</u>
        AS YOU READ.

✿ COLOR CODE!!

✿ USE SYMBOLS: ✢ ✳ ◆ ➜

✿ MAKE MARGINAL
   NOTES.

< main
  idea

++Good
  point!

POWER NOTES AND POWER WRITING

1. Animals
    2. Dog
        3. Cairn Terrier
        3. Golden Retriever
    2. Cat
        3. Siamese
        3. Tabby

Two types of animals live in my backyard. The first . . . . .

MATHEMATICS PROBLEM SOLVING GUIDE

Question

Plan

Plan in writing

Answer

Check

CHAPTER 6

Ladybird Beetle

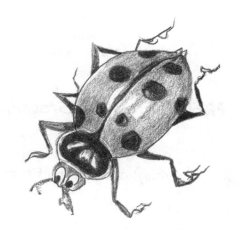

Purpose

- **Process:** To become familiar with the strategies of Selective Highlighting and Underlining, Power Notes, Power Writing, and the Mathematics Problem Solving Guide and to be able to apply these strategies in other classes.

- **Content:** To determine the eating habits of the ladybird beetle.

CRISS^{SM} Learning Plan

Prepare: *Mind Streaming*
Be Involved: *Selective Highlighting and Underlining*
Organize: *Power Notes*
Apply: *Power Writing and
Mathematics Problem Solving Guide*

Implementation

__PREPARE__: *Mind Streaming (B-2)*

- With a partner, mind stream everything you know about the ladybird beetle (ladybug) and record below.

__BE INVOLVED__: *Selective Highlighting and Underlining (A-6)*

- Your teacher will show you how to highlight (or underline) selectively the most important information from a selection.

- On pages 48 and 49 of this book, read "Tough Terminator #2, Ladybird Beetle," and selectively highlight or underline the most important information. If you can, label your highlighting with Power numbers. NOTE: DO NOT HIGHLIGHT IN YOUR *TOUGH TERMINATORS* BOOK, but open it to pages 8 and 9 so you can see the illustrations. Then, respond to the prompts in the boxes on pages 48 and 49.

- Also, as you read, look for details which verify or disprove the information you and your partner mind streamed. Where your information is proved, put a "✔" in the margin. If anything you said is disproved, put an "✗" in the margin. (These marks are just to help you remember.) Share this information with your partner when you have finished reading.

Ladybird Beetle

FAST FACTS

► **Kind of Animal . . .**
    Insect
► **Order of Insects . . .**
    Beetles
► **Family of Beetles . . .**
    Coccinellids or "Ladybird" beetles
► **Weight . . .**
    Less than 1/100th of an ounce
► **Length . . .**
    Between .03 and .71 inches
► **Lifespan . . .**
    One to three years

Predators don't have to be big like the tiger. They don't have to live in wild jungles or forests, either. One of the world's hungriest predators is a small animal you can find in your back yard—the ladybird beetle, or ladybug.

The habitats where ladybird beetles live all have one thing in common: food. A few kinds of ladybugs eat leaves and fungus, but most are predators. They catch aphids, mites, and tiny insects called scales.

What information did you learn from this illustration?

What information did you learn from this picture?

Like other insects, ladybird beetles live their lives in two major stages. After they hatch from eggs, they are called **larvae** (LAR-VEE). Ladybird beetle larvae look a little like caterpillars. They can't fly like adult beetles can, but they have healthy appetites. A hungry larva can devour 300 aphids in a single day.

As it grows, a larva moults or "sheds its skin" four or five times. After several weeks, it forms a cocoon. Inside this safe refuge, the larva grows into an adult. Like larvae, adult ladybird beetles eat hundreds of aphids and other insects every day.

Where does this map indicate you would NOT find ladybird beetles? Why do you think they cannot live there?

There are over 4,500 species of ladybird beetles. They live all over the world and in many different kinds of places, or habitats.

Many predators have powerful eyes and ears to help them find their prey, but not ladybird beetles. Both larvae and adult beetles find other animals by "bumping into" them. Larvae can starve to death if they don't bump into something within a day or two after they hatch. If adults don't find food, they fly to a new plant or a new place and search for food there.

Draw a picture of the Ladybird Beetle.

What information did you learn from this picture?

What does this drawing illustrate?

Farmers love ladybird beetles. In the 1890s, Australian ladybird beetles were imported to California so they could eat a kind of scale that was destroying orange trees. The ladybird beetles ate so many that they saved California's citrus industry. Using ladybird beetles and other predators to eat pests helps farmers to avoid using dangerous pesticides to protect their crops.

ORGANIZE: *Power Notes (A-5)*

- Watch as your teacher models how to transfer the highlighted/underlined information in the selection to Power Notes. Now, transfer your own highlighting to Power Notes. Use the space below.

APPLY 1: *Power Writing (D-4)*

· Look at your Power Notes and determine which two Power 2s you wish to write about in your Power Writing summary.

· Plan the information you want to write about in a Power organizer such as the one below. You may wish to delete or add more Power 3 information.

1. *Ladybird Beetle*
    2.
        3.
        3.
    2.
        3.
        3.
1. *Ladybug* (This will be your concluding sentence relating to your first sentence.)

· Write your Power Paragraph in the space provided.

_____

_____

_____

_____

_____

_____

_____

APPLY 2: *Mathematics Problem Solving Guide (C-5)*

- Your teacher will model for you how to use the following organizer to solve this first problem.

MATHEMATICS PROBLEM 1

According to the selection on the ladybird beetle, the "ladybug" can consume about 300 small insects in one day. In 1890, two million ladybugs were imported to California in hopes that they could save the orange crop which was being destroyed by a kind of scale, a small insect. In the three months from June 1 to August 31, 1890, the ladybugs ate so many insects that they saved the citrus crop. Figure out how many nasty little pests were eaten by the corps of ladybird beetles.

- Fill in the Problem Solving Form below, with your teacher, so you have a model to follow when you do the next problem.

1. QUESTION

| |
| |

2. MATHEMATICAL PLAN

3. PROBLEM SOLVING PLAN (Pre-writing)

4. WRITTEN ANSWER plus the process used to determine the answer. (Start by changing the question in box 1 to a statement.)

```

```

5. CHECK YOUR ANSWER. Does your answer make sense?

```

```

MATHEMATICS PROBLEM 2

According to the author, "A hungry [ladybird beetle] larva can devour _____ aphids in a single day." If Spot and her 16 brothers and sisters consumed 107,100 aphids before entering their cocoons, for how many weeks did they remain in the larval stage? (NOTE: Assume each larva eats the same number of aphids.)

1. QUESTION

```

```

2. MATHEMATICAL PLAN

3. PROBLEM SOLVING PLAN (Pre-writing)

4. WRITTEN ANSWER plus the process used to determine the answer. (Start by changing the question in box 1 to a statement.)

5. CHECK YOUR ANSWER. Does your answer make sense?

- Now, apply the Problem Solving Guide to a word problem from your own mathematics class.

Check Your Understanding

MULTIPLE CHOICE: *(Circle the letter of the correct response.)* What would be the best subheading for the last paragraph of this chapter?

    A. How to Control Ladybird Beetles
    B. Ladybird Beetles to the Rescue
    C. Stages of the Ladybird Beetle
    D. Hungry Ladybird Beetles

WRITING ITEM: Summarize the eating habits of the ladybird beetle. Use details and information from the article to support your answer.

_____

_____

_____

_____

_____

_____

_____

REFLECTION

- Talk about how the strategies of Selective Highlighting, Power Notes, and Power Writing helped you to understand and remember the information in the selection on the ladybird beetle.

- What could you have done to be more successful with your learning?

_____

_____

_____

Apply This to Other Classes

- Think about how you can apply these learning strategies to your other classes and record your thoughts below.

_____

_____

_____

_____

_____

- Remember to save samples of successful applications to share with the class and to place in your folder.

 KEY TO LEARNING No. 1

 KEY TO LEARNING No. 2

 KEY TO LEARNING No. 3

 KEY TO LEARNING No. 4

Meet the Chapter 7 Strategies "At a Glance"

ANTICIPATION GUIDE

Agree	Disagree	Statement
✔		1.
	✔	2.
	✔	3.

READ-AND-SAY-SOMETHING

Read.

Say something.

Read.

Say something.

Read.

Say something.

TWO-COLUMN NOTES

Main Ideas	Details
Tiger	
Ladybug	

RAFT

R: Role of writer

A: Audience

F: Format

T: Topic + strong verb

North Pacific Giant Octopus

Purpose

- **Process:** To become familiar with the strategies Anticipation Guide, Read-and-Say-Something, Main Idea–Detail Notes, and RAFT, and be able to apply these strategies in other classes.

- **Content:** To determine why the North Pacific giant octopus is considered a skilled hunter.

CRISS℠ Learning Plan

Prepare: *Anticipation Guide*
Be Involved: *Read-and-Say-Something*
Organize: *Anticipation Guide and*
Main Idea–Detail Notes
Apply: *RAFT*

Implementation

PREPARE: *Anticipation Guide*

- The Anticipation Guide is a reading strategy in which you respond to several statements to activate your thoughts and opinions about a topic you will be studying. The next animal you are going to read about is the North Pacific giant octopus.

- On the Anticipation Guide below, check (✔) whether you AGREE or DISAGREE with the six statements. After you have INDEPENDENTLY completed the Anticipation Guide, have a discussion with your partner to see if you agreed or disagreed with one another. Be prepared to share your opinions with the class.

	AGREE	DISAGREE	STATEMENT
1	_____	_____	The octopus is a vertebrate because it has a flexible backbone.
2	_____	_____	There are about 200 species of octopus.
3	_____	_____	The giant octopus has over 2,000 suction cups on its six arms.
4	_____	_____	The octopus has no teeth.
5	_____	_____	The octopus can carry up to 12 crabs at the same time.
6	_____	_____	Scuba divers have often been attacked and bitten by octopuses.

BE INVOLVED: *Read-and-Say-Something (B-4)*

- Now read the "Tough Terminator #3, North Pacific Giant Octopus" selection to see if your opinions were correct. Your teacher will give you directions on how to read the selection with your partner.

ORGANIZE 1: *Anticipation Guide Revisited*

- After reading the selection, complete the following guide. For each of the original Anticipation Guide statements, if you found your response was correct, check (✔) that you found SUPPORT for your answer and write the information that proves you were right in the EVIDENCE column. If you were wrong, check (✔) that you found NO SUPPORT for your answer and write the correct information to the right in the EVIDENCE column. You will end up with six true statements in the EVIDENCE column when you have finished.

- Were you curious to find out if your answers were correct? This strategy arouses your interest, sets purposes for your reading, and helps to clear up any misconceptions you may have on the topic. These are all very important to your learning!

Support	No Support	Evidence
1. _____	_____	_____
2. _____	_____	_____
3. _____	_____	_____
4. _____	_____	_____
5. _____	_____	_____
6. _____	_____	_____

ORGANIZE 2: *Main Idea–Detail Notes (C-7)*

- Complete the Two-Column Notes chart on the following page to organize the information from the selection on the octopus.

MAIN IDEA—DETAIL NOTES

MAIN IDEA	DETAIL

APPLY: *RAFT (D-5)*

- RAFT is an acronym; each letter represents a part of a writing assignment. R is the Role of the writer or author; A is the Audience, the person or people to whom the writer is writing; F is the Format in which the author writes; and T is the Topic selected by the writer. On the following page, write the RAFT paper described below.

      Role =   Octopus
      Audience =   Scuba Diver
      Format =   Letter
      Topic =   Apologize for scaring the diver

- Work with a partner. Use the Role Definition Matrix to help you plan before you write your RAFT. Be prepared to share your letter with the class.

ROLE DEFINITION MATRIX		
Personality: *Who am I and what are some aspects of my personality?*	**Attitude:** *What are my feelings, beliefs, ideas, concerns?*	**Information:** *What do I know that I need to share in my writing?*

RAFT PAPER

Check Your Understanding

MULTIPLE CHOICE: *(Circle the letter of the correct response.)* With which of the following statements below would the author of this book MOST LIKELY AGREE?

     A. Octopuses are social creatures.
     B. Scuba divers should fear octopuses.
     C. Octopuses have strong backbones.
     D. Octopuses are smart.

WRITING ITEM: The author infers that the octopus is a skilled hunter. Use details from the chapter to support this inference.

_____

_____

_____

_____

_____

_____

_____

_____

REFLECTION

- Think about how the strategies of Anticipation Guide, Read-and-Say-Something, Main Idea–Detail Notes, and RAFT helped you to understand and remember the information in the selection on the octopus.

- What could you have done to be more successful in your learning?

_____

_____

_____

_____

Apply This to Other Classes

- Think about how you can apply these learning strategies to help you study in your other classes. Record your thoughts below.

_____

_____

_____

_____

- Remember to save samples of successful applications to share with the class and to place in your folder.

KEY TO
LEARNING
No. 1

KEY TO
LEARNING
No. 2

KEY TO
LEARNING
No. 3

KEY TO
LEARNING
No. 4

Meet the Chapter 8 KEY TO LEARNING and Strategies "At a Glance"

METACOGNITION

Knowing if you KNOW

and

Knowing what to do
if you DON'T

STICKY NOTES

Use sticky notes to mark
important places.

TWO-COLUMN NOTES

Fix-up Strategy	Explanation

METACOGNITION JOURNAL

This diagram created using Inspiration® 7.5 by Inspiration Software®, Inc.

KEY TO LEARNING No. 5– Metacognition Through Writing and Discussing

Purpose

- **Process:** To become familiar with the KEY TO LEARNING No. 5– Metacognition and understand how to use it through writing and discussing to become a better reader.

CRISS℠ Learning Plan

Prepare: *Write and Discuss*
Be Involved: *Mark "Clunks" with Sticky Notes*
Organize: *Two-Column Notes*
(Fix-up Strategy–Explanation or Clarification)
Apply: *Metacognition Journal*

Implementation

PREPARE: *Write and Discuss*

- Up to now, the KEYS TO LEARNING have been fairly easy to understand. *Metacognition* is a word that most people (even teachers!) don't know. Here is some information which will help you get started.

> METACOGNITION is recognizing that you *understand* what you are reading, seeing, or hearing. It is also knowing when you do not understand AND knowing what to do to gain understanding.
>
> METACOGNITIVE SKILLS can be learned. They are the strategies which will help you monitor your understanding and make learning easier for you. As you go through this chapter, you will probably discover you already know and are using some metacognitive skills.

- All readers, no matter how well or poorly they read, have some materials they can understand pretty well (a novel, a magazine, comics, baseball statistics, a picture book). They can clickity-click across the pages easily. On the other hand, most readers have some materials they have difficulty understanding, and the clickity-click turns to a CLUNK. What kinds of "clunks" do you run into with your reading? Maybe you don't have enough background knowledge or you don't know the purpose (two of our important KEYS TO LEARNING). Maybe the material is boring. List your clunks below.

_____

_____

_____

- Share your clunks with the class. You probably have a lot of the same problems.

- When you are reading and come to a "clunk," what do you do? Give up? Read again? In the following space, write what you do.

_____

Continue ➜

- Share your ideas (other than "give up") with the class and start to develop a list of FIX-UP strategies.

- Remember to add to the list as you complete the learning plan for this chapter.

BE INVOLVED: *Identifying Clunks Using Sticky Notes*

- Follow along as your teacher reads through the two rattlesnake selections on the next page and models for you what good and poor readers do. As your teacher reads, complete the following Two-Column Chart.

What poor readers do:	What good readers do:

CANEBRAKE RATTLESNAKE

Ranging from Maine to Texas, the timber rattlesnake is the most widely occurring venomous snake in the eastern U. S., but only its lowland variety, called the canebrake rattlesnake, is found south from Live Oak and Jacksonville to Gainesville [Florida]. A few recent sparse records from panhandle Florida may represent released captive snakes.

Canebrake refers to its wetland habitats that are dominated by native American bamboo grasses, commonly called switchcane. The canebrake rattlesnake is distinctive with bold black chevrons across a light grey to tan background color. Often it has a rusty line down the middle of its back. The unconnected zigzag chevrons and rusty streak identify it from the eastern diamondback, which has bold yellow diamonds surrounding black pigment with brown centers. The tail of the canebrake is jet black, from whence it gets its nickname, velvet-tail.

The canebrake rattlesnake is nocturnal in contrast to the day-loving eastern diamondback. It lives mostly in creek bottoms, wet flatwoods and swamps, but occasionally is found in the upland habitats of the eastern diamondback. Once thought not to be as venomous as the latter species, recent studies have shown certain populations to be highly toxic. A bite from the canebrake should be considered as serious as a bite from the eastern diamondback.

PIGMY RATTLESNAKE

The pigmy rattlesnake is so small and different in looks from the other rattlesnakes, that it is often mistaken by the uninitiated for a non-venomous snake. Seldom more than 20 inches long (record is 31 inches), this tiny snake has puny rattles to match. Don't expect to see or hear its rattles without making a special effort. What it lacks in size, the pigmy rattler makes up in being feisty. It may strike repeatedly, thrash about, then make a dash for safety. It is so different from other rattlesnakes that biologists have put it in a separate genus. The head is not nearly so broad as in most pit vipers, and the vertical pupil and facial pit are difficult to see on the tiny, boldly marked face.

There is no easy way to learn to identify the pigmy rattlesnake except by learning its color pattern. It is a small, grayish, "mottled" rattlesnake having dozens of round, evenly spaced black or dark brown blotches distributed in offset rows all over the body. Usually, but

not always, individuals have a distinctive, thin, orange stripe down the middle of the back which is most conspicuous between the black blotches. The rattle usually can be seen on close inspection, but be careful not to get too close.

Also called ground rattler, the pigmy rattlesnake is found throughout Florida and on many offshore islands. It flourishes in flatwoods habitats with lots of ponds and swampy streams, but is also common in sand hill habitats in the vicinity of limesink depressions and ponds. It feeds on a large number of small animals including insects, spiders, centipedes, frogs, toads, lizards, snakes, nestling birds, and mice. Its bite is painful and produces swelling and discoloring, which usually subsides in a few days to a week depending upon severity. Fortunately, the bite of the tiny pigmy rattlesnake is the least dangerous of all Florida's pit vipers and no deaths have been recorded, but medical attention should always be sought for venomous snake bites.

Photos and text reprinted with permission of the author, D. Bruce Means, Ph.D., President and Executive Director of the Coastal Plains Institute and Land Conservancy and Adjunct Professor, Department of Biological Science, Florida State University, Tallahassee, Florida.

- Now that you know what good readers do, read through this selection on the eastern diamondback rattlesnake, and mark clunks, fix-up strategies, and places where you checked your understanding.

EASTERN DIAMONDBACK RATTLESNAKE

Largest of all rattlesnakes (individuals up to 7 feet long have been measured), the eastern diamondback has been recorded throughout Florida from Pensacola to the Marquesas and Tortugas, isolated islands west of Key West. It lives primarily in upland habitats, which once were predominantly longleaf pine forests growing on clay hills, sand hills, and flatwoods. In south Florida, its upland habitat was originally dominated by slash pine. Often the eastern diamondback is found in grassy/shrubby habitats on coastal islands and once in a while even in hardwood forests. Most of the longleaf forests have disappeared, but the eastern diamondback can survive in the man-created habitats that have replaced longleaf pine, such as shortleaf and loblolly pine forests, overgrown pastures, and abandoned lots; providing there is enough acreage to sustain a population.

The venom of the eastern diamondback is unusually neurotoxic for a pit viper. That, combined with the large dose, makes this the most dangerous snake in Florida, but recent field studies have shown that the eastern diamondback is a Dr. Jekyll/Mr. Hyde of the venomous snake world. The normally gentle snake relies on its camouflage to go unnoticed, lying still and silent unless practically stepped upon. Once threatened, however, it engages in several behaviors that are designed to warn its enemy to stay away. In addition to rattling, it swells its body to look as large as possible, making a long hissing sound while sucking air into its lungs, and it spreads its ribs to flatten the lower half of its body. When maximally aroused, it may lift the upper half of its body into the air about 12-15 inches. If approached within striking range, about  2/3 of its body length, it will strike and envenomate its enemy, but it often strikes to warn and squirts a fine jet of smelly liquid at its enemy from musk glands at the base of the tail. The odor has been described as rancid peanut butter.

The eastern diamondback does not den up for the winter like northern and western snakes, but individuals take refuge from cold weather underground in stump holes, tree tip-up mounds or burrows of the gopher tortoise and armadillo from November through March. Spring emergence begins in February and is completed by late March. Snakes are more often seen at this time, and especially during breeding season, August and September, when males search for females. In October and November, rattlers move back to the same overwintering sites used in previous winters.

An average of 14 young are born in August and September. Young rattlers are about 16 inches in total length. Broods as small as 6 and as large as 29 have been recorded. Newborn rattlers grow quickly and can be nearly three feet long by the following summer, depending upon their rate of success finding mice and rats to eat. Young rattlers shed their skin three or four times in their first year, adding one segment to their rattle string each time. As they mature in three or four years, their shedding rate declines to about twice per year. Average density in native habitat has been estimated at one snake per twenty acres, but extremely dense island populations have been recorded at one to five individuals per acre.

Eastern diamondbacks eat exclusively warm-blooded prey including particularly the cotton mouse, cotton rat, grey and fox squirrels, marsh rabbit, and eastern cottontail. Very few birds are taken, probably because they would fly away and leave no trails to follow when struck. The indigo snake is a major predator, as are the kingsnake, black racer, coachwhip, red tail hawk, and great horned owl. Today, habitat loss and fragmentation, and direct killing by gunshot, auto tires, and other human implements are the major sources of mortality and population decline.

Photos and text reprinted with permission of the author, D. Bruce Means, Ph.D., President and Executive Director of the Coastal Plains Institute and Land Conservancy and Adjunct Professor, Department of Biological Science, Florida State University, Tallahassee, Florida.

• Did you discover any new fix-up strategies?

<u>ORGANIZE</u>: *Two-Column Notes (C-7) (Fix-up Strategy–Explanation or Clarification)*

• You have done a lot of work with clunks and fix-up strategies. Now, it is time to organize your fix-up strategies into Two-Column Notes. The notes have been started for you. Complete them by adding all of the fix-up strategies you have used so far (in the left-hand column) and an explanation or clarification (in the right-hand column). Mark this page with a sticky note for quick reference.

FIX-UP STRATEGY	EXPLANATION OR CLARIFICATION
1. Slow down	1. Change your reading speed for difficult material. Textbook material usually requires slower reading than a novel or short story.
2. Read on	2. Sometimes the author will explain information further into the paragraph or selection. The author might provide examples or more details as you continue to read.
3. Reread	3.

- Now that you have your fix-up strategies ready to use, let's review the whole process which successful, metacognitive readers use.

PROCESS FOR SUCCESSFUL, METACOGNITIVE READERS

1. Survey the reading selection to determine the topic. Look at headings, subheadings, visuals, and graphics. *(Author's Craft)*

2. Think about what you already know. *(Background Knowledge)*

3. Determine a purpose for reading. Establish some questions you want answered. *(Purpose Setting)*

4. Keep your purpose in mind as you read and monitor your understanding. *(Active Learning)*

5. If you hit a CLUNK, stop reading and plan your next move. Survey the fix-up list on the preceding page and pick a strategy. *(Metacognition)*

6. Did your fix-up strategy work? If yes, you are on your way! If no, go back to step 5 and pick another fix-up strategy. *(Metacognition)*

- Notice how the KEYS TO LEARNING fit into the successful reader's plan!!!

APPLY: *Metacognition Journal*

Directions for eight-page Metacognition Journal

NOTE: Use 18" x 24" paper
1. Fold paper left to right (24" in half)
2. Fold top to bottom (18" in half)
3. Fold right to left (12" in half)
4. Open paper back up to first fold (step 1) and cut inward from center of fold side to center mark, "c"
5. Lay paper flat, unfolded with slit going lengthwise from left to right.
6. Pull cut sections straight up and let one section fold to the front and one to the back of the cut.
7. Hold on to the two ends of the paper and push toward the center, so both sides of the center slit open up.
8. Keep pushing in until the two folds, "a" and "b", meet.
Bingo! You have an eight-page booklet!

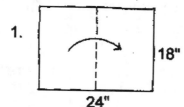

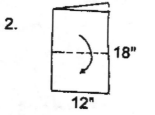

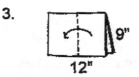

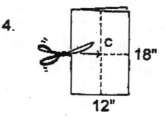

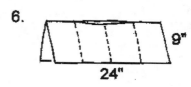

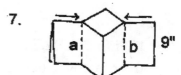

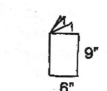

• Now, we need to turn your eight-page booklet into a Metacognition Journal.

1. Label your booklet "Metacognition Journal," and add your own cover design. At the bottom of the cover, put your name and class period.

2. Format the next six pages so they look like the page to the right.

3. During the next week or so (your teacher will give you a due date), it will be your job to complete the six metacognition journal entries in this booklet.

4. Bring the completed journal to class. On the back page of your booklet describe (a) how you have become a more metacognitive reader and (b) which fix-up strategies worked best for you.

CLASS:

BOOK:

CLUNK:

FIX-UP STRATEGY(IES) USED:

HOW DID IT WORK?

Check Your Understanding

MULTIPLE CHOICE: *(Circle the letter of the correct response.)* In this chapter, the authors say "successful readers are metacognitive." What does this mean?

    A. Successful readers monitor their understanding of text and know what to do when they do not understand.

    B. Successful readers never have clunks.

    C. Successful readers read very carefully and slowly.

    D. Successful readers never reread.

WRITING ITEM: According to the *Project CRISS*^{SM} *for Students* authors, to be a successful reader you need to do more than open a book and start reading. Using details from this chapter, explain what successful readers do to prepare for reading and to understand what they have read.

_____

_____

_____

Continue ➔

_____

_____

_____

_____

_____

REFLECTION

- Think about KEY TO LEARNING No. 5–Metacognition and how it helped you understand the information in your other classes.

- What could you have done to be more metacognitive and successful with your learning?

_____

_____

_____

_____

Apply This to Other Classes

- Think about how you can apply Metacognition to your other classes. Record your thoughts below.

_____

_____

_____

_____

_____

- Remember to save samples of successful applications to share with the class and to place in your folder.

Meet the Chapter 9 Strategies "At a Glance"

THINK-PAIR-SHARE

STICKY NOTES

Use sticky notes to mark important places.

CONCEPT OF DEFINITION MAP

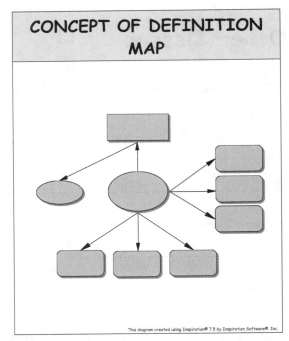

This diagram created using Inspiration® 7.5 by Inspiration Software®, Inc.

ONE-SENTENCE SUMMARIES

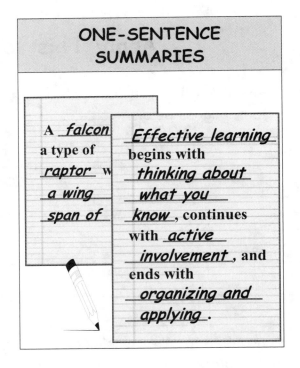

A *falcon* a type of *raptor* w a *wing* span of

Effective learning begins with *thinking about* *what you* *know*, continues with *active involvement*, and ends with *organizing and applying*.

Aplomado Falcon

Purpose

- **Process:** To become familiar with the strategies of Think–Pair–Share, Sticky Notes, Concept of Definition Map, and One-Sentence Summary, and to be able to apply these strategies in other classes.

- **Content:** To discover what makes the aplomado falcon one of the world's most spectacular raptors.

CRISS^{SM} Learning Plan

Prepare:	*Think–Pair–Share*
Be Involved:	*Sticky Notes*
Organize:	*Concept of Definition Map*
Apply:	*One-Sentence Summary*

Implementation

PREPARE: *Think–Pair–Share (B-8)*

- The Think–Pair–Share strategy will activate your background knowledge on your favorite bird. In the space below, write about your favorite bird by describing it and telling why you like it.

Favorite bird: _____

_____

_____

_____

- Next, share your writing with a partner.

- Finally, you may be asked to share with the whole class.

BE INVOLVED: *Sticky Notes (B-7)* (preparing for the Concept of Definition Map) *(E-3)*

- Your teacher is going to be introducing or reviewing the Concept of Definition Map strategy. Knowing what kinds of details you are to find while reading the selection on the aplomado falcon will set a purpose for your reading. In the space below, record the types of information for which you will be looking.

_____

_____

- Read the "Tough Terminator #4, Aplomado Falcon." Using sticky notes or scratch paper, record the types of information found in each paragraph. You will be using this information as the "Category" labels on the Concept of Definition Map on page 83.

- Watch the "Critterman" DVD on falcons and record on scratch paper any additional information you learn about the falcon. Did you discover any new <u>types</u> of information?

<u>ORGANIZE</u>: *Concept of Definition Map (E-3), Modified*

*   After reading and viewing, complete the Concept of Definition Map on the falcon with a partner. You may have to modify the categories to fit the information you read and saw. Discuss what information should be included. Be prepared to share your map with the class.

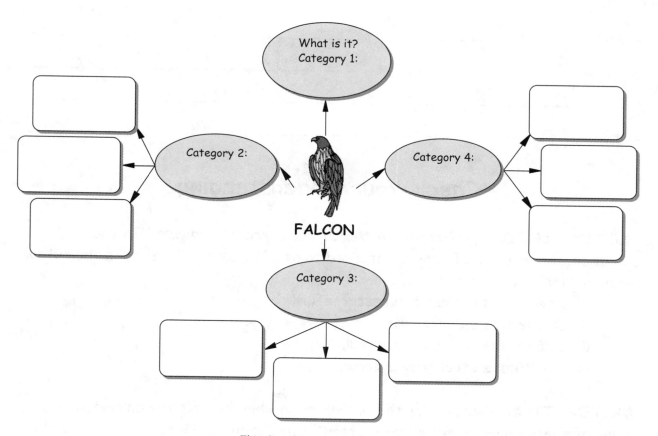

This diagram was created using Inspiration® 7.5 by Inspiration Software®, Inc.

<u>APPLY</u>: *One-Sentence Summary (D-3)*

*   Write two One-Sentence Summaries using the information on the falcon you included in your Concept of Definition Map. Be prepared to share your sentences with the class. Complete your One-Sentence Summaries on the lines provided on the next page.

Summary template 1: A _____ is a kind of _____ that . . . .

Summary 1: _____

_____

_____

_____

Summary template 2: The _____ wanted to . . . but . . . so . . . .

Summary 2: _____

_____

_____

_____

Check Your Understanding

MULTIPLE CHOICE: *(Circle the letter of the correct response.)* In the selection, the aplomado falcon is referred to as a "top gun." What does the author mean by "top gun"?

 A. One that is patient and resourceful.

 B. One that is old and wise.

 C. One that is fast and powerful.

 D. One that is steel gray in color.

WRITING ITEM: What does the author mean when he says the aplomado falcon is one of earth's most spectacular raptors? Use details and information from the selection and the DVD to support your answer.

_____

_____

_____

_____

Continue ➜

_____

_____

_____

_____

REFLECTION

- Talk about how the strategies Think–Pair–Share, Sticky Notes, Concept of Definition Map, and One-Sentence Summaries helped you understand and remember the information in the selection on the aplomado falcon.

- What could you have done to be more successful with your learning?

_____

_____

_____

_____

Apply This to Other Classes

- Think about how you can apply these learning strategies to your other classes. Record your thoughts below.

_____

_____

_____

_____

- Remember to save samples of successful applications to share with the class and to place in your folder.

Meet the Chapter 10 Strategies "At a Glance"

STICKY NOTES

Use sticky notes to mark important places.

QUESTION-ANSWER RELATIONSHIPS (QARs)

Right There	Author and You
Think and Search	On My Own

QARs + TWO-COLUMN NOTES

Main Ideas	Details
1. Author & You	1. _____ _____
2. Think & Search	2. _____ _____

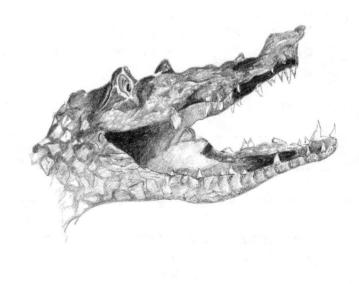

Saltwater Crocodile

Purpose

- **Process:** To become familiar with the strategies of Sticky Notes and Question–Answer Relationships (QARs), to understand how the QAR strategy fits with Two-Column Notes, and to be able to apply these strategies in other classes.

- **Content:** To determine what makes the saltwater crocodile a skilled hunter.

CRISS[SM] **Learning Plan**

Prepare:	*Analyze Visuals*
Be Involved:	*Sticky Notes*
Organize:	*QARs*
Apply:	*Two-Column Notes with QARs*

Implementation

PREPARE: *Analyze Visuals*

- With a partner, take a look at the four crocodile illustrations found in the selection on the saltwater crocodile. Talk to your partner about what you see and how you feel. Write these thoughts in the space provided. Also, include any questions you and your partner have about the crocodile.

_____

_____

_____

_____

_____

- Now, you and your partner need to put yourself in the position of the crocodile in the two photographs. What do you think he is thinking? On a sticky note placed above each picture draw a "balloon," like you see above cartoon characters in the newspaper, and write in it what you think the crocodile is thinking.

BE INVOLVED: *Sticky Notes (B-7)*

- Your teacher will show you how to use sticky notes to help you remember key information from a selection and to help you relate the new information in the article to information you already know or think you know.

- Read "Tough Terminator #5, Saltwater Crocodile" and mark SURPRISING or INTERESTING facts you discover about "saltie." Remember, write on the sticky note why this information surprised or interested you. NOTE: DO NOT WRITE IN YOUR *TOUGH TERMINATORS* BOOK.

- Also, as you read, look for information which relates to your comments and questions in the preceding "Prepare" section. Cross out incorrect information, put a check (✔) by verified information, and answer your questions.

ORGANIZE: *Question-Answer Relationships (QARs) (B-3)*

- Listen carefully as your teacher explains the four types of QARs and models how to write them.

- The task for your group is to write four QARs based on the saltwater crocodile selection. Write your questions and the correct responses in the space which follows.

Right There: _____

_____

_____

Answer: _____

_____

_____

Think and Search: _____

_____

_____

Answer: _____

_____

_____

Author and You: _____

_____

_____

Answer: _____

_____

_____

Continue ➥

On My Own: _____

_____

_____

Answer: _____

_____

_____

- Now, each group will have a chance to read one of its questions to all the other groups. (Don't tell which type of QAR.) The other groups will first try to identify the type of question. After they have determined the type, they will answer the question. Your group and your teacher will determine if the responses are correct.

- If, for any question, the groups cannot come to agreement about what type of QAR it is, students in the class should edit and/or rewrite the question, so it is definitely one of the four QAR types.

<u>APPLY</u>: *QARs (B-3) with Main Idea—Detail Notes (C-7)*

- In Chapter 7, where you worked with the selection about the giant octopus, you learned how to create Two-Column Notes. To make these notes even better, include QARs in the left-hand column instead of just the Power 2 categories of information. The most important QAR types to use are **Think and Search** and **Author and You**. Both of these will help you think and pull together the details in the selection. Try it! Use the Two-Column Note organizer on the next page to develop notes on the saltwater crocodile.

QARs with MAIN IDEA–DETAIL NOTES

Main Idea QARs	QAR Answers

Check Your Understanding

MULTIPLE CHOICE: *(Circle the letter of the correct response.)* Which of the following statements is BEST SUPPORTED by the article?

    A. Crocodiles should fear humans.

    B. Crocodile skins are of little value.

    C. Crocodiles feed on domestic animals.

    D. Crocodiles carefully chew and digest their food.

WRITING ITEM: Why are crocodiles known to be very skilled hunters? Use details and information from the article to support your answer.

_____

_____

_____

_____

_____

_____

_____

_____

REFLECTION

- Talk about how the strategies of Sticky Notes, QARs, and Main Idea–Detail Notes with QARs helped you to understand and remember the information in the selection on the saltwater crocodile.

- What could you have done to be more successful with your learning?

_____

_____

_____

_____

Apply This to Other Classes

- Think about how you can apply these learning strategies to your other classes. Record your thoughts below.

_____

_____

_____

_____

_____

- Remember to save samples of successful applications to share with the class and to place in your folder.

Meet the Chapter 11 Strategies "At a Glance"

PRE- AND POST-READING LEARNING LOG ENTRIES

PRE: Before reading, I know . . .

POST: After reading, I discovered I was RIGHT . . . , but I also found out I was WRONG when I said . . . . I learned some NEW INFORMATION, too. . . .

MARGINAL PICTURE NOTES with STICKY NOTES

Draw pictures on sticky notes to illustrate important information.

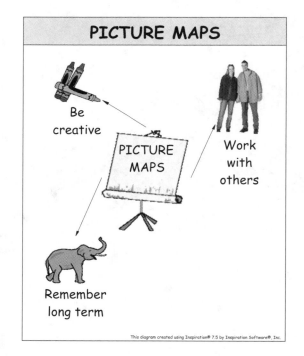

When I wake Corky up in the morning, he leaps off his pillow and jumps up and down until I put him out. Outside, he runs from one end of our yard to the other until I convince him to come in and eat breakfast. After breakfast, he wants to play catch. Finally, my arm gives out and, when he realizes I am done playing, he chases his tail around for a while, then dashes upstairs to play with another member of the family. My dog Corky is really energetic.

PICTURE MAPS

Be creative

PICTURE MAPS

Work with others

Remember long term

This diagram created using Inspiration® 7.5 by Inspiration Software®, Inc.

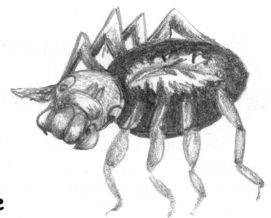

Community Spider

Purpose

- **Process:** To become familiar with the strategies of Pre- and Post-reading Learning Log Entries, Marginal Picture Notes, and Picture Maps and to be able to apply these strategies in other classes.

- **Content:** To determine what makes the community spider unique in the family of spiders and how this characteristic benefits the community spider.

CRISS^{SM} Learning Plan

Prepare:	*Pre-reading Learning Log Entry*
Be Involved:	*Marginal Picture Notes with Sticky Notes*
Organize:	*Picture Mapping*
Apply:	*Post-reading Learning Log Entry*

Implementation

PREPARE: *Pre-reading Learning Log Entry (D-1)*

- To make the most of reading, we have to think about what we already know, or think we know, about a topic. Next, we need to connect the new information from the selection to our background knowledge and make any necessary corrections.

- The next predator selection we will be reading is the community spider. Consider what you know about the word "community" and what you know about spiders. Now, write what you *predict* the community spider is like. (Remember, this *Tough Terminators* book usually talks about where and how the animals live, what and how they hunt, and how they interact with man and other animals. Include this information in your predictions.)

_____

_____

_____

_____

_____

_____

_____

BE INVOLVED: *Marginal Picture Notes with Sticky Notes*

- As you read the next *Tough Terminators* selection on the community spider, we want you to do some planning for the "organizing" strategy Picture Mapping.

- Your teacher will either provide you with sticky notes (which you can place in the margin next to each paragraph) or have you write/draw your "marginal" notes by the paragraph numbers provided on the following page.

- Now read "Tough Terminator #6, Community Spider" and draw (on the sticky note or below) representations or pictures of the main ideas from each of the five paragraphs. If you use the sticky notes, stick them by the numbers below when you are done with all of your illustrations.

1.   2.

3.   4.

5.

ORGANIZE: *Picture Mapping (C-3)*

- Your teacher will talk to you about Picture Mapping. In small groups, you will complete a map which represents the entire community spider selection. Then, your group will report on the information using your map.

- Work with your partners to decide on the best illustrations to represent (1) the main ideas of the selection and (2) the purpose listed at the beginning of this chapter.

APPLY: *Post-reading Learning Log Entry (D-1)*

- Look back to the Pre-reading Entry you recorded at the beginning of this chapter. Now that you have read and organized the information on the community spider, write a summary of what you have learned. Tell about any of the misinformation you may have written when you made your initial prediction about this spider.

_____

_____

_____

_____

_____

_____

_____

_____

Check Your Understanding

MULTIPLE CHOICE: *(Circle the letter of the correct response.)* According to the information in the chapter, the community spider lives in the following parts of the world.

    A. North and South America

    B. Southern Africa, Asia, and Madagascar

    C. Asia, Australia, North America

    D. South America, Madagascar, and North Africa

WRITING ITEM: What did the scientists in the selection discover to be the predator benefits of "social spiders"? Use details and information from the selection to support your answer.

_____

_____

_____

_____

_____

_____

_____

REFLECTION

• Talk about how the strategies Pre- and Post-reading Learning Log entries, Marginal Picture Notes, or Picture Mapping helped you understand and remember the information in the selection on the community spider.

• What could you have done to be more successful with your learning?

_____

_____

_____

Apply This to Other Classes

- Think about how you can apply these learning strategies to your other classes and record your thoughts below.

_____

_____

_____

_____

_____

- Remember to save samples of successful applications to share with the class and to place in your folder.

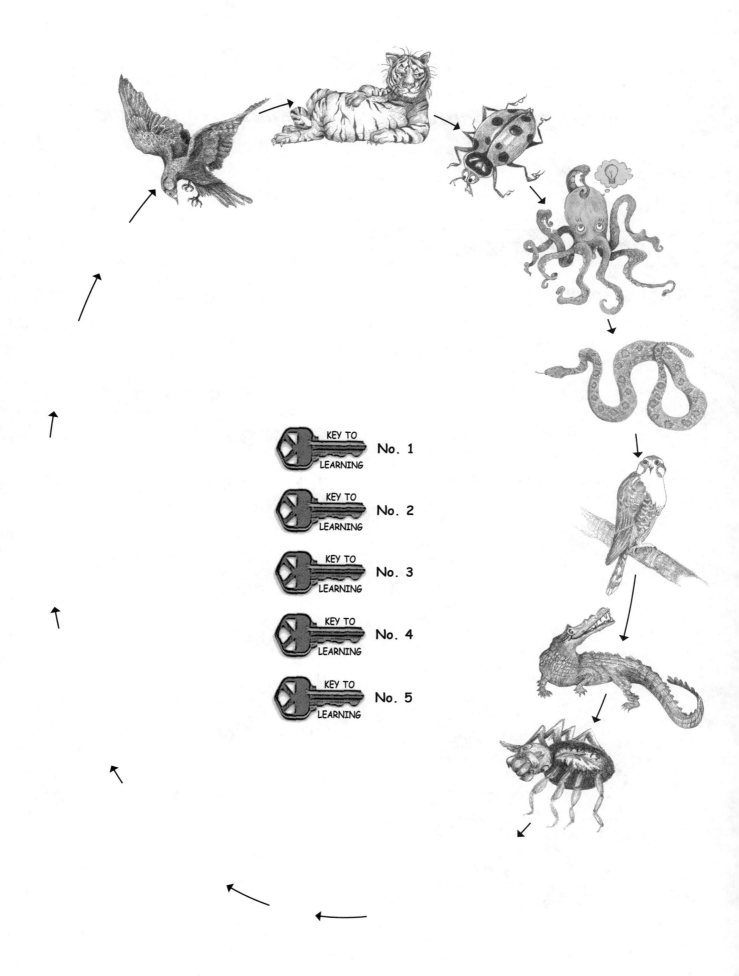

KEY TO LEARNING No. 1

KEY TO LEARNING No. 2

KEY TO LEARNING No. 3

KEY TO LEARNING No. 4

KEY TO LEARNING No. 5

Meet the Chapter 12 Strategies "At a Glance"

ABC BRAINSTORMING

What I know...

A: _____

B: _____

C: _____

D: _____

•
•
•

STORY PLAN

Setting	
Characters	
Goal	
Problem	
Events	
Resolution	

CHAPTER 12

Grizzly Bear

Purpose

- **Process:** To become familiar with the strategies of ABC Brainstorming, Watch and Record, Story Plans, and writing and to be able to apply these strategies in other classes.

- **Content:** To determine the grizzly's relationship with humans, the diet of the grizzly bear, and what is involved in grizzly hibernation.

CRISS℠ Learning Plan

Prepare:	*ABC Brainstorming*
Be Involved:	*Watch and Record*
Organize:	*Story Plan*
Apply:	*Write a Short Story*

Implementation

PREPARE: *ABC Brainstorming*

- The next predator you are going to study is the grizzly bear. Think about everything you know about grizzly bears or think about bears in general, if you are not familiar with the grizzly. After each letter of the alphabet below, write down something you know which starts with that letter. For example, next to "A" you could write "Attack people." You can't write many details, but you should be able to explain your answer, "I read that last summer, in Glacier National Park, Montana, several people were attacked by grizzlies while they were hiking and passed too close to a mama grizzly's cubs."

- If you cannot think of anything to go with one of the letters, skip it and go on to the next letter. As you go, you may think of more information and return to skipped letters.

A: _____   J: _____   S: _____

B: _____   K: _____   T: _____

C: _____   L: _____   U: _____

D: _____   M: _____   V: _____

E: _____   N: _____   W: _____

F: _____   O: _____   X: _____

G: _____   P: _____   Y: _____

H: _____   Q: _____   Z: _____

I: _____   R: _____

- Compare your brainstorming with that of a partner. If your partner has information for one of the letters that you don't, you can add your partner's information to your list.

- ABC Brainstorming is a good strategy to use when you are trying to remember details about a topic. Some students use it before writing responses to essay questions on a test.

BE INVOLVED: *Watch and Record*

- As you WATCH the "Critterman" DVD on grizzly bears, listen carefully and RECORD in the space provided below information you learn about the grizzly that SURPRISES you. The space below is divided into three columns, each one headed with one of the content purposes listed at the beginning of this chapter. Record SURPRISES in each column. Is there information which is different from what you and your partner brainstormed on the preceding page?

Relationship with Humans	Diet	Hibernation

- Discuss the SURPRISING information from the DVD with your class or in a small group. Add new information to your Three-Column Notes.

Critterman comes face to face with a grizzly bear skull.

©2004, Critterman's World.
Used with permission.
www.crittermansworld.com

ORGANIZE: *Story Plan (C-8)*

- Story Plans work well to organize information from a fictional story, a novel, a current event, or an event in history. They also work well as organizers for writing stories. Stories usually have the following components:

STORY PLAN COMPONENTS
Setting (time and place)
Characters (about whom the story is told)
Goal (what the main character wants to achieve)
Problem (what "road blocks" the main character encounters)
Events (the most important things that happen in the story)
Resolution (Does the main character reach his/her goal?)

- Most fictional stories have the elements listed above. Take a look at them as they occur in this summary of <u>Moby Dick</u> by Herman Melville.

Ahab, captain of a whaling ship, is obsessed with killing a huge white whale, Moby Dick. Captain Ahab hunts down and attacks the whale with harpoons. Moby Dick fights back, fighting for his life. He is severely wounded, but still too strong for the crew. He destroys the ship Pequod and most of the shipmates. Only one survives to tell the story. Moby Dick pulls Captain Ahab to the bottom of the sea. He is not captured by the captain.

Moby Dick	Moby Dick Perspective	Captain Ahab Perspective
Setting	the open sea	the open sea, on the ship Pequod
Characters	Moby Dick, Captain Ahab, and shipmates	Moby Dick, Captain Ahab, and shipmates
Goal	not be caught by Captain Ahab	conquer the great, white whale
Problem	Ahab is obsessed and determined to conquer Moby Dick.	Moby Dick is too big and strong for the small whaling ship.
Events	Ahab is obsessed with killing the whale. He finds the whale and attacks. Moby Dick is wounded. The whale battles the crew and destroys the ship. Moby Dick submerges, pulling Captain Ahab to a watery grave.	Ahab is obsessed with killing the whale. He finds the whale and attacks. Moby Dick is wounded. The whale battles the crew and destroys the ship. Moby Dick submerges, pulling Captain Ahab to a watery grave.
Resolution	Moby Dick is not caught by Captain Ahab. He reaches his goal.	Ahab and his crew, except one, all die. Ahab does not reach his goal.

- Notice that the Story Plan is completed in two ways, according to Moby Dick and according to Captain Ahab. For most stories, current events, and events in history, the Story Plan can be completed in different ways, depending on the perspective.

- Before you use the Story Plan as an organizer for a short story you will write on the grizzly, you need an opportunity to use the Story Plan to take notes. Use the following Story Plan to record information from a current event article your teacher will give to you.

CURRENT EVENT: _____

Setting	
Characters	
Goal	
Problem	
Events	
Resolution	

- Now, write a paragraph summary of the current event based on the notes you recorded in the Story Plan form.

_____

_____

_____

_____

_____

_____

_____

- Your next project will be to write a fictional story which involves grizzly bears. To be realistic, your story will need to include facts about the grizzly. You can use information you learned from the DVD and from other resources provided by your teacher.

- Use the following Story Plan to organize the information for your short story.

Story Title:_____

Setting	
Characters	
Goal	
Problem	

Continue ➤

Events	
Resolution	

APPLY: *Write a Short Story Based on Your Story Plan*

- Now that you have your story planned, your teacher will play the DVD one more time so you can write down any facts you would like to include in your story. You may use the following space or add to the notes you took in the "Be Involved" section of this chapter.

- Use the information you recorded on previous pages and in your Story Plan to write your story.

_____
_____
_____
_____
_____
_____
_____
_____
_____
_____
_____
_____
_____
_____
_____
_____
_____
_____
_____

_____

_____

_____

_____

_____

_____

_____

_____

_____

_____

- Use another sheet of paper if you need additional space.

Check Your Understanding

MULTIPLE CHOICE: _(Circle the letter of the correct response.)_ Critterman says grizzlies use their long claws to:

    A. clean their teeth.

    B. catch tourists.

    C. turn over rocks in search of food.

    D. dig holes to store their food.

WRITING ITEM: According to information given in the DVD, the grizzly, during hibernation, can survive through the winter without food or water. What adaptations does Critterman say the grizzly bear has made in order to survive? Use information provided in the DVD to support your answer.

_____

_____

Continue ➡

_____

_____

_____

_____

_____

REFLECTION

- Talk about how the strategies of ABC Brainstorming, Watch and Record, the Story Plan, and writing helped you to understand and remember the information in the Critterman DVD about the grizzly bear.

- What could you have done to be more successful with your learning?

_____

_____

_____

_____

Apply This to Other Classes

- Think about how you can apply these learning strategies to your other classes and record your thoughts below.

_____

_____

_____

_____

- Remember to save samples of successful applications to share with the class and to place in your folder.

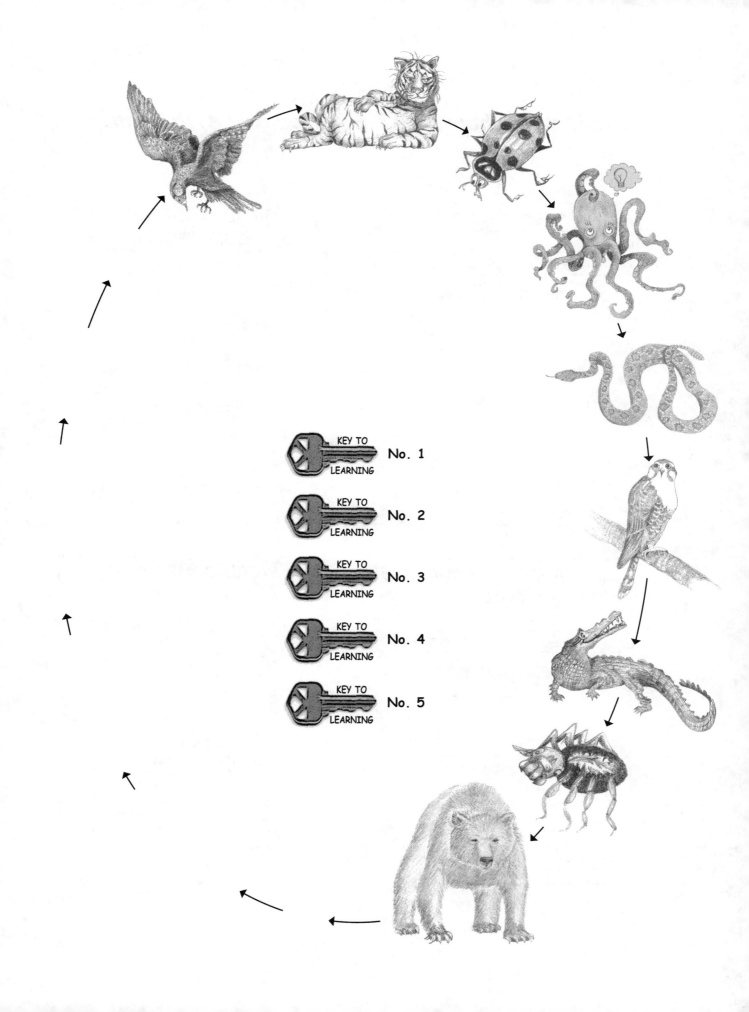

KEY TO LEARNING No. 1

KEY TO LEARNING No. 2

KEY TO LEARNING No. 3

KEY TO LEARNING No. 4

KEY TO LEARNING No. 5

Meet the Chapter 13 Strategies "At a Glance"

STICKY NOTES

Use sticky notes to mark important places.

READ-AND-SAY-SOMETHING

Read.

Say something.

Read.

Say something.

Read.

Say something.

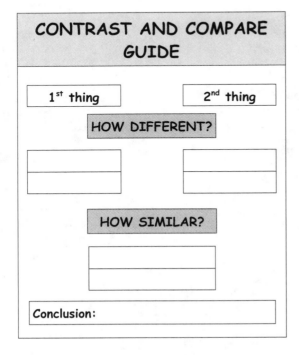

CONTRAST AND COMPARE GUIDE

1st thing	2nd thing

HOW DIFFERENT?

HOW SIMILAR?

Conclusion:

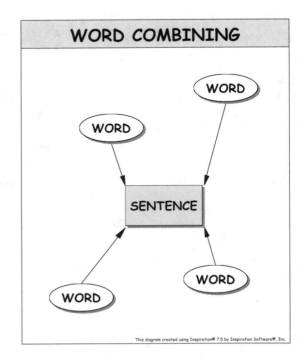

WORD COMBINING

WORD

WORD

SENTENCE

WORD

WORD

This diagram created using Inspiration® 7.5 by Inspiration Software®, Inc.

Great Barracuda

Purpose

- **Process:** To become familiar with the strategies of Visualization, Sticky Notes, Read-and-Say-Something, the Contrast and Compare Guide, and Word Combining and to be able to apply these strategies in other classes.

- **Content:** To determine the similarities and differences between the great barracuda and other predators in *Tough Terminators*.

CRISS^{SM} Learning Plan

Prepare: *Visualization*
Be Involved: *Sticky Notes or Read-and-Say-Something*
Organize: *Contrast and Compare Guide*
Apply: *Word Combining*

Implementation

<u>PREPARE</u>: *Visualization*

- Visualization is a powerful strategy to help you think about what you already know about a topic and to remember new information as you learn it. Your teacher will help you visualize the animal coming up in the next selection. First, close your eyes, then your teacher will set the scene and ask you some questions.

- After you have visualized the barracuda, its food, and its surroundings, turn to your partner and see if you can describe the video clip you created in your mind which starred the barracuda.

<u>BE INVOLVED</u>: *Your Choice: Sticky Notes (by yourself) or*
Read-and-Say-Something (B-4) (with a partner)

- Before you start reading the selection "Tough Terminator #7, Great Barracuda," look at all of the illustrations, including the map that marks where the great barracuda lives, and read the "Fast Facts." With your partner or table group, share where your vision appears to be correct and where it appears to be incorrect.

- Now, using either Sticky Notes or Read-and-Say-Something, actively read through the selection creating pictures in your mind for each paragraph. Sometimes, it helps to close your eyes after reading each paragraph, so you have time to come up with a vision.

<u>ORGANIZE</u>: *Contrast and Compare Guide (C-2)*

- Your teacher will explain the parts of the Contrast and Compare Guide and model how to use it.

- Using the information you learned in the great barracuda selection, compare this terminator with the tiger, the first terminator you studied. See how much of the information about both animals you can fill in without rereading. When you can't remember any more information, refer to the selections to check your entries and to add more information.

CONTRAST and COMPARE GUIDE

1. TIGER	2. GREAT BARRACUDA

HOW DIFFERENT?

1   2

With regard to . . .

HOW SIMILAR?

With regard to . . .   1 & 2

Conclusion:

<u>APPLY</u>: *Word Combining (E-6)*

- Your teacher will explain to you how to write a summary using key vocabulary terms from a selection. We call this process Word Combining.

- Write from one to three sentences about the great barracuda in the space provided. Include the following words in your Word Combining and underline them. *(Remember to include clues about the words in your sentences, so someone who has not read the great barracuda selection will still understand your message.)*

Word combining words: *tropical, grassbeds, loner, ciguatera*

_____

_____

_____

_____

_____

_____

_____

_____

Check Your Understanding

MULTIPLE CHOICE: *(Circle the letter of the correct response.)* With which of the following statements below would the author of Tough Terminators MOST LIKELY DISAGREE?

    A. The great barracuda is found in every tropical ocean except the eastern Pacific Ocean.

    B. In the past 100 years, only one person has died from a barracuda attack.

    C. Large barracudas hunt for their prey independently.

    D. Barracuda is a popular food enjoyed by many people all over the world.

WRITING ITEM: How are the barracuda and the tiger DIFFERENT and ALIKE? Use details and information from your Contrast and Compare Guide and from pages 6-7 and 18-19 in *Tough Terminators* to support your answer.

_____

_____

_____

_____

_____

_____

_____

_____

REFLECTION

- Talk about how the strategies Visualizing, Sticky Notes or Read-and-Say-Something, Contrast and Compare Guide, and Word Combining helped you understand and remember the information in the selection on the great barracuda.

- What could you have done to be more successful with your learning?

_____

_____

_____

_____

_____

Apply This to Other Classes

- Think about how you can apply these learning strategies to your other classes and record your thoughts below.

_____

_____

_____

_____

_____

_____

- Remember to save samples of successful applications to share with the class and to place in your folder.

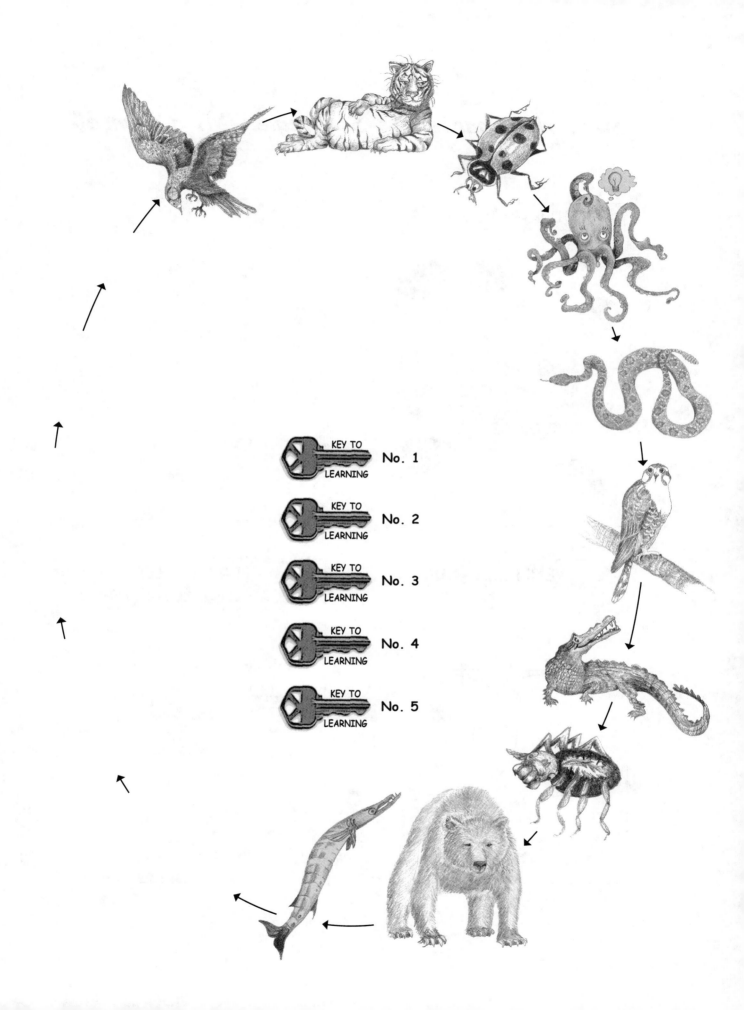

KEY TO LEARNING No. 1

KEY TO LEARNING No. 2

KEY TO LEARNING No. 3

KEY TO LEARNING No. 4

KEY TO LEARNING No. 5

Meet the Chapter 14 Strategies "At a Glance"

THINK-PAIR-SHARE

VENN DIAGRAM

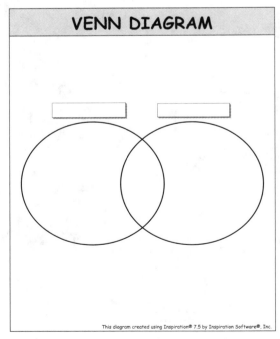

PERSPECTIVE LEARNING LOG ENTRY

Pitcher Plant

Purpose

- **Process:** To become familiar with the strategies of Think–Pair–Share, Venn Diagram, and Perspective Learning Log Entry, to try a strategy of your choice to stay actively involved as you read, and to be able to apply these strategies in other classes.

- **Content:** To understand that plants, as well as animals, can be predators.

CRISS℠ Learning Plan

Prepare:	*Think–Pair–Share*
Be Involved:	**Your Choice**
Organize:	*Venn Diagram*
Apply:	*Perspective Learning Log Entry*

Implementation

PREPARE: *Think–Pair–Share (B-8)*

- Your teacher will use the strategy Think–Pair–Share to bring out your background knowledge before you read the next selection. First, you will spend a minute or two thinking about the following question: How can a plant be a predator? Write down your thoughts and any questions you might have. If you are not sure how this can happen (you are free to make some guesses), put a question mark after your comments.

_____

_____

_____

_____

_____

- Next, you and your partner will share your ideas. Add to your list anything your partner listed with which you agree. Can you confirm any of your partner's guesses? Can your partner confirm your guesses? If so, you can remove the question marks.

- Finally, you will share your paired information with the whole class.

BE INVOLVED: *Your Choice*

- Your teacher will have you do a quick review of all of the strategies you have used so far. Select one strategy you think works to keep you *actively involved* with the reading and write the name below. In the empty "At a Glance" box on page 122, record the name and a quick sketch of your strategy as a reminder.

_____

- Read "Tough Terminator #8, Pitcher Plant." Remember to use the strategy you selected!

• How did your strategy work for you?

_____

_____

_____

• Did you learn anything which either confirms or refutes the information you or your class listed during the Think–Pair–Share brainstorming? Place a "✔" by correct ideas and correct any misinformation.

<u>ORGANIZE</u>: *Venn Diagram (C-4)*

• Your teacher will provide information about how to develop a comparison map called the "Venn Diagram."

• Complete the Venn Diagram on the following page by comparing the pitcher plant to the ladybug (Terminator #2).

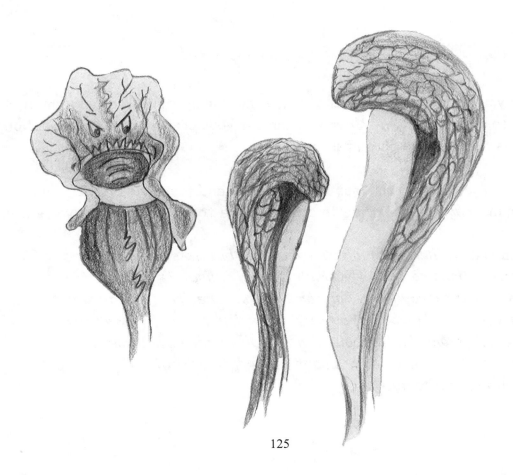

VENN DIAGRAM

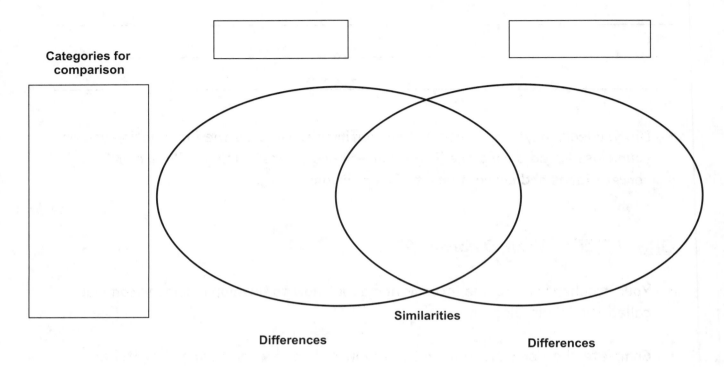

Categories for comparison

Similarities

Differences

Differences

This diagram was created using Inspiration® 7.5 by Inspiration Software®, Inc.

APPLY: *Perspective Learning Log Entry (D-2)*

- To help you learn and remember the information in your Venn Diagram, it is helpful to write about it. When you can use your creativity and imagination, writing is even a more powerful tool.

- Use the information from your Venn Diagram and from the pitcher plant chapter in *Tough Terminators* to complete the following Perspective Learning Log Entry.

    You are a pitcher plant minding your own business in a boggy area of Florida. Along comes a fly which is nearly blind. It bumps into you and falls onto a nearby leaf. For some reason, the fly starts talking to you as if you are a ladybug. You need to explain to the fly how you are different from the ladybug even though you do have some things in common. If you are really smart, you will figure out a way to lure the fly into your pitcher.

Perspective Learning Log Entry:

_____

_____

_____

_____

_____

_____

_____

Check Your Understanding

MULTIPLE CHOICE: *(Circle the letter of the correct response.)* Within this chapter there is a sign, "Pitcher Plant Picking Prohibited." Why has this graphic been included?

　　　To inform readers that:
- A. pitcher plants are poisonous.
- B. pitcher plants can cause allergies.
- C. pitcher plants have thorns that can cut the skin.
- D. pitcher plants are helpful and need to be protected.

WRITING ITEM: How are the pitcher plant and the ladybird beetle DIFFERENT? Use information and details from pages 8-9 and 20-21 in *Tough Terminators* to support your answer.

_____

_____

_____

_____

_____

_____

Continue ➦

_____

_____

REFLECTION

• Talk about how the strategies Venn Diagram, the Perspective Learning Log Entry, and the strategy you selected to "Be Involved" helped you understand and remember the information in the selection on the pitcher plant.

• What could you have done to be more successful with your learning?

_____

_____

_____

_____

_____

Apply This to Other Classes

• Think about how you can apply these learning strategies to your other classes. Record your thoughts below.

_____

_____

_____

_____

_____

• Remember to save samples of successful applications to share with the class and to place in your folder.

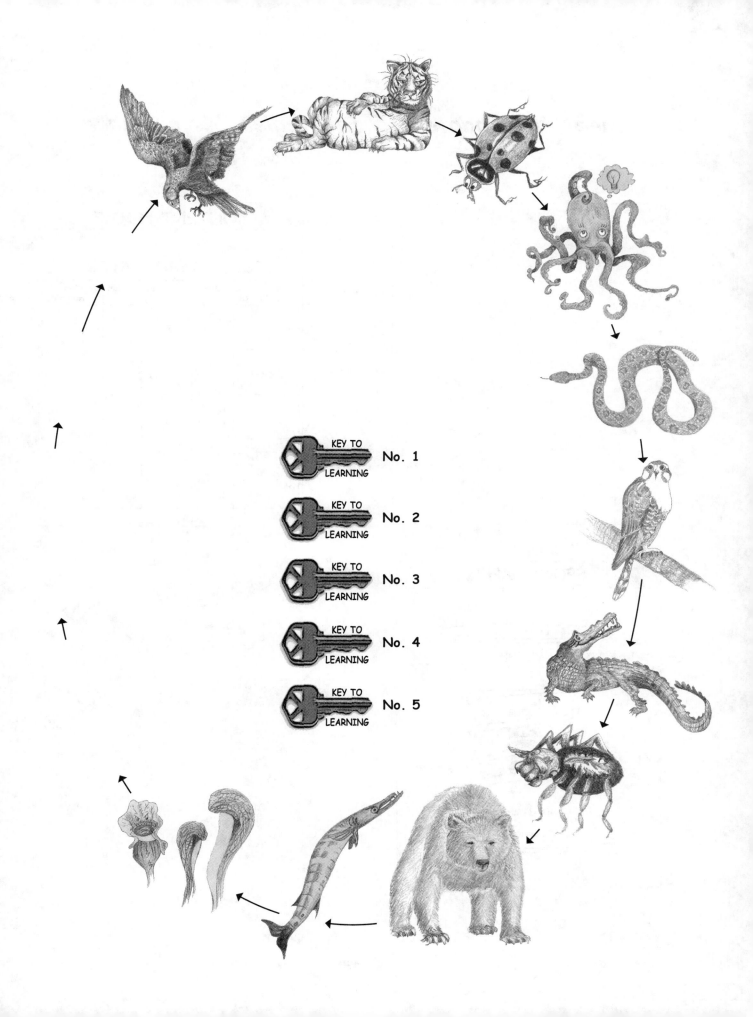

KEY TO LEARNING No. 1

KEY TO LEARNING No. 2

KEY TO LEARNING No. 3

KEY TO LEARNING No. 4

KEY TO LEARNING No. 5

Meet the Chapter 15 Strategies "At a Glance"

CONTENT FRAME

TOUGH TERMINATORS

PREDATORS	Diet	How They Hunt	Habitat	Relationship to Humans
tiger				
ladybug				
pitcher plant				
grizzly bear				

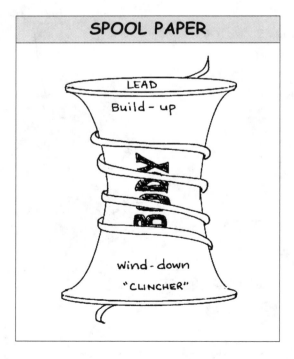

SPOOL PAPER

LEAD
Build-up
BODY
wind-down
"CLINCHER"

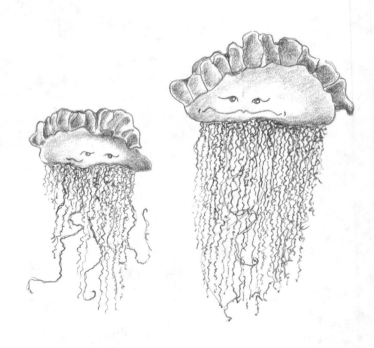

CHAPTER 15

Siphonophore

Purpose

- **Process:** To become familiar with the strategies of Content Frames and Spool Papers, to try out a strategy of your choice to stay actively involved as you read, and to be able to apply these strategies in other classes.

- **Content:** To determine how the siphonophore hunts and to identify its other unique features.

CRISS^{SM} Learning Plan

CRISS^{SM} Learning Plan

Prepare: *"Who Am I?" Game*
Be Involved: **Your Choice**
Organize: *Content Frame*
Apply: *Spool Paper*

Implementation

PREPARE: *"Who am I?" Game*

- Your teacher will provide information about the next Tough Terminator, one fact at a time. After each fact, your group will have a chance to guess the name of the animal. Talk about the information before making your guess. Be specific by giving the complete name of the predator, for example, "robin" rather than "bird."

BE INVOLVED: *Your Choice*

- As you read "Tough Terminator #9, Siphonophore," pay close attention to the *types* of information the author provides, things such as "physical appearance" or "food." Remember, this author uses photographs, graphics, maps, charts, and words to give you information.

- List the types of information on sticky notes or on a sheet of scratch paper, so you can refer to them when you begin to create your notes in a Content Frame.

ORGANIZE: *Content Frame (C-1)*

- Working with your partner or group, fill in the types or categories of information across the top of the following frame. If you have more categories than this chart allows or if you need more space to write, recreate the frame on another piece of paper.   It is possible that you will have fewer types of information. In the "Predators" column, write the names of three other terminators you have already studied. This frame will help you compare the four.

CONTENT FRAME COMPARING FOUR TOUGH TERMINATORS

Predators						
Siphonophore						

- Using the selections on the siphonophore and the comparison predators, fill in the information for each box of your chart. If you cannot find some of the information you need in the *Tough Terminators* book, check other resources in your media center.

- The Content Frame note-taking organizer works well with texts or other written materials which are divided into chapters or sections where the types of information presented are basically the same. Talk with your classmates to determine texts in other classes which might work well for taking Content Frame notes.

APPLY: *Spool Paper (D-6)*

- Your teacher will review the Spool Paper format with you. Together, you, the rest of the class, and your teacher will develop an introductory paragraph. Copy this paragraph onto the following Spool Paper Planning Sheet. Complete the rest of the Planning Sheet using information from your Content Frame.

- Now, on a separate piece of paper, write a Spool Paper by yourself based on the information from your Spool Paper Planning Sheet.

SPOOL PAPER PLANNING SHEET

Topic: _____

Introductory paragraph

Lead *(Power 0):*_____

_____

Thesis/Opinion *(Power 1 which introduces the two Power 2s):*_____

_____

_____

Body paragraph 1

*(Power 2a):*_____

_____

Supporting details *(Power 3s):*_____

_____

_____

Body paragraph 2

*(Power 2b):*_____

_____

Supporting details *(Power 3s):*_____

_____

_____

Concluding paragraph

Restatement of Thesis/Opinion *(Power 1):*_____

_____

_____

Conclusion *(Power 0):*_____

_____

_____

Check Your Understanding

MULTIPLE CHOICE: *(Circle the letter of the correct response.)* With which statement would the author MOST LIKELY AGREE?

    A. Siphonophores are generally small.

    B. Siphonophores live only in shallow water.

    C. Siphonophores are crafty hunters of prey.

    D. Siphonophores are completely harmless.

WRITING ITEM: According to the author, siphonophores have strategies for catching prey. Use information and details from the article to support this conclusion.

_____

_____

_____

_____

_____

_____

_____

_____

REFLECTION

• Talk about how the strategies Content Frame, Spool Paper, and the strategy you selected to "Be Involved" helped you understand and remember the information in the selection on the siphonophore.

• What could you have done to be more successful with your learning?

_____

_____

_____

Continue ➜

_____

_____

_____

Apply This to Other Classes

- Think about how you can apply these learning strategies to your other classes and record your thoughts below.

_____

_____

_____

_____

_____

- Remember to save samples of successful applications to share with the class and to place in your folder.

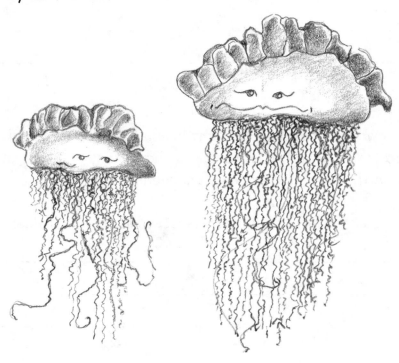

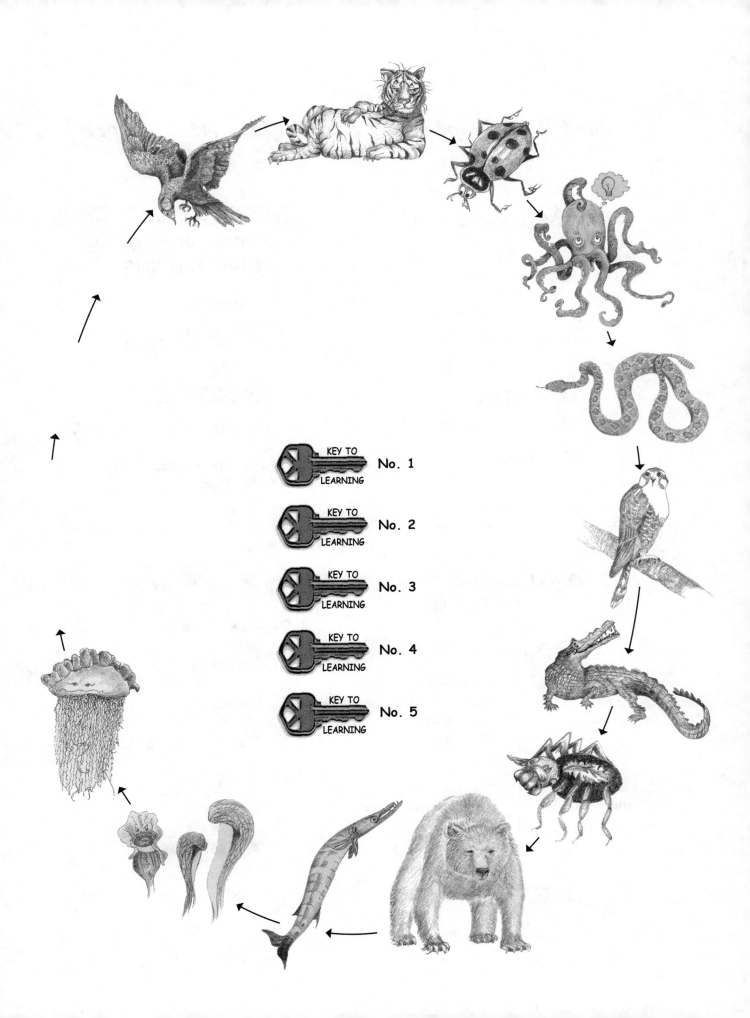

KEY TO LEARNING No. 1

KEY TO LEARNING No. 2

KEY TO LEARNING No. 3

KEY TO LEARNING No. 4

KEY TO LEARNING No. 5

Meet the Chapter 16 Strategies "At a Glance"

CRISS℠ LEARNING PLAN

☞ PREPARE.

☞ BE INVOLVED.

☞ ORGANIZE.

☞ APPLY.

SELECTIVE UNDERLINING AND HIGHLIGHTING

UNDERLINE
KEY WORDS
AS YOU READ.

✿ COLOR CODE!!

✿ USE SYMBOLS: ✛ ✳ ◆ ➜

✿ MAKE MARGINAL
NOTES.

< main idea

++Good point!

CONCLUSION–SUPPORT NOTES

Conclusion	Support
Predators are **helpful** to humans.	• By eating pests, they prevent the spread of diseases & help production of crops.
Predators are **harmful** to humans.	• They compete with people for food.

RAFT

R: Role of writer

A: Audience

F: Format

T: Topic + strong verb

Gray Wolf

Purpose

- **Process:** To learn how to develop a CRISS^{SM} Learning Plan, to become familiar with the strategies of Selective Highlighting and Underlining, Conclusion–Support Notes, and RAFT, and to be able to apply these strategies to other classes.

- **Content:** To be able to debate the author's conclusion that "wolves are not such bad guys after all."

CRISS^{SM} Learning Plan

Prepare:	*Discussion and Two-Column Notes*
Be Involved:	*Selective Highlighting or Underlining*
Organize:	*Conclusion–Support Notes*
Apply:	*RAFT*

Implementation

PREPARE 1: *Discussion and Two-Column Notes*

- With your group, talk about whether wolves are "good guys" or "bad guys." Discuss information you have read about wolves in fairy tales, novels, short stories, magazine articles, the newspaper, or personal experiences. Write examples of good and bad wolf behavior in the Two-Column Notes format which follows.

Wolves are good guys	Wolves are bad guys

- With your group members, determine whether you think the wolf is basically good or bad. Put a star (✳) at the top of that column and be ready to support your point of view with the two most convincing pieces of evidence you have in your notes.

PREPARE 2: *More Discussion and Two-Column Notes*

- Your teacher will play the "Critterman" DVD on wolves. This segment will give you some background information about wolf packs and the social order within the packs. In the space below, record three pieces of new information you learned from the DVD.

_____

_____

_____

BE INVOLVED: *Selective Highlighting and Underlining (A-6)*

- Your teacher will review with you the guidelines for Selective Highlighting and Underlining.

- As you read the "Tough Terminator #10, Gray Wolf," found on the following pages (and later when you read the "perspective" selections), determine the author's opinion of wolves (good guys/bad guys), write this opinion statement at the top of the selection, then selectively highlight or underline the support for that opinion. <u>NOTE</u>: DO NOT WRITE IN YOUR *TOUGH TERMINATORS* BOOK, but open to pages 24 and 25 so you can see the illustrations and then respond to the prompts in the boxes.

- Next, read one of the perspective selections found on pages 144-147 (after the gray wolf selection). Your teacher will let you know which selection to read. As you did with the *Tough Terminator* selection, determine the author's point of view (wolves are good guys/bad guys). Write this at the top of the page, then selectively highlight or underline the supporting information.

- Now, look at the details you underlined in both the gray wolf and perspective selections to see if they verify or disprove the information your group recorded in the Two-Column Notes. Where your information is *proved*, put a "✔" in the margin. If anything is *disproved*, put an "✗" through the item. (These marks are just to help you remember.)

FAST FACTS

► **Species Name . . .**
   Canis lupus
   (KAY-NIS LOOP-US)
► **Kind of Animal . . .**
   Mammal
► **Order of Mammals . . .**
   Carnivores
► **Family of Carnivores . . .**
   Canids or "Dogs"
► **Weight . . .**
   33 to 176 pounds
► **Length . . .**
   4 to 6 feet
► **Lifespan . . .**
   8 to 20 years

GRAY WOLF

No other "terminator" has inspired more fear than the wolf. In stories like "Little Red Riding Hood," wolves are villains that attack grandmothers and devour small children. But in recent times, people have discovered that wolves are not such bad guys after all.

Does this picture make you think the wolf is a "good guy" or a "bad guy"? Why?

Does this illustration make you think the wolf is a "good guy" or a "bad guy"? Why?

Wolves eat different things, depending on where they live. In desert areas, they pounce on rabbits and other small prey. Where larger prey is common, wolves hunt moose, beaver, and caribou. But wolves are fairly small, and they're not fast runners. In order to kill large animals, they often hunt in social groups called **packs**.

Each wolf pack contains between two and 20 wolves. The pack is highly organized, and it's led by two wolves—the **alpha male** and the **alpha female**. The two alpha wolves are usually the only pack members that mate, and they also lead the pack in hunting and feeding. To catch a caribou or a moose, several wolves may rush at the animal and overwhelm it. At other times, one or two wolves may trap an animal by herding it toward other wolves.

Why do you think wolves no longer live in the locations colored blue on this map?

Wolves once roamed over most of the northern hemisphere—from the Arctic Circle to Mexico and even the deserts of the Middle East. Today, large wolf populations are found only in parts of Canada, Alaska, Minnesota, Iran, southeastern Europe, and the former Soviet Union.

Like many other predators, wolves are highly intelligent. They howl to stay in touch with each other. Younger wolves learn how and where to hunt from older wolves in the pack. As long ago as 10,000 years, people learned that they could tame and breed wolves as workers and companions. All modern dogs—from poodles to German shepherds—are descended from the tamed wolves of long ago.

There are hundreds of stories about wolves attacking and killing people. Almost all of these stories are false. Probably the biggest reason people have feared wolves is because wolves compete with us as predators. Wolves eat deer that hunters would like to shoot for themselves. Sometimes wolves feed on domestic livestock. They don't know that cows belong to a rancher or dairy farmer. To wolves, a cow simply looks like dinner.

But people and wolves can—and do—live together peacefully. Over a thousand wolves live in Minnesota, many of them near farms. In Italy, wolves live within 30 miles of Rome, a city of almost three million people. When people start to understand these predators, they realize that wolves are really shy, intelligent, and amazing animals.

Does this picture make you think the wolf is a "good guy" or a "bad guy"? Why?

Perspective: Hunter

I have lived in this valley for over forty years and, ever since I
was a young boy, I have been hunting in the surrounding forests.
In the last few years, since the introduction of wolves into this
area, I have noticed that the deer and elk populations have really
declined.

I know the ranchers think the wolves are eating their sheep and
cattle, but I think they are also eating the game that used to be
so plentiful. Those wolves hunt in packs and need a lot of wild
game to satisfy them. It is just not fair. Every year I have
been able to shoot a deer until last year. My family saves a lot
of money by eating wild game.

The wolves come onto the land that is ours, eat our game and
livestock, and we cannot even shoot them, since they are
protected by the Endangered Species Act. No, it's just not right.

I think this community should contact the folks at the U.S. Fish
and Wildlife Service and demand they remove the wolves from this
area.

Perspective: Member of
            "Restore the Gray Wolf Coalition"

I think it is a travesty what we have done to wolves in this nation. Wolves were present in North America for tens of thousands of years. They co-existed with large game, such as moose, elk, deer, and bison, just fine. During the 1800s the wolf populations were nearly wiped out thanks to bounties which originated in the eastern states as early as the middle of the 1600s. "Woolfers" in Montana Territory killed as many as 100,000 wolves annually between 1870 and 1877. By the 1930s, other than a few packs in northern Minnesota, virtually no wolves remained in the 48 contiguous states.

Had it not been for the Endangered Species Act (ESA) in 1973, which legally protected wolves, I am sure the gray wolf would now be classified as extinct. The U.S. Fish and Wildlife Service (FWS) has established three wolf restoration programs. I know there is resentment in this area for having wolves re-introduced here, but honestly, this was their land before we arrived and developed it. I think, no, I know from other restoration plans that wolves, people, game, and livestock can co-exist successfully.

As long as the wolves in this area are listed as an endangered or threatened species, the FWS, along with our state and tribal wildlife agencies, is responsible for managing the wolf populations. They use management tools such as live traps and dart rifles. They monitor wolves with radio collars and move, trap, or even shoot troublesome animals.

I think we need to focus on management of wolves rather than removal.

Perspective: Cattle Rancher

I know this is probably going to surprise many members of this community, but I support keeping the wolf pack in this county. You all know I have been a rancher for a lot of years, and during that cold dry winter we had two years ago, I did lose two cows to wolves. But, honestly folks, I lost more cattle to coyotes in previous years than all the ranchers in this valley have lost to wolves since this restoration process began. And, maybe you haven't noticed, but with the addition of wolves, the coyotes have all disappeared.

I might add, too, when I lost those two animals two years ago, the Defenders of Wildlife, that private, non-profit conservation organization, compensated me for my loses. That never happened when those dang coyotes enjoyed a steak dinner on me!

Most of you know my daughter, Becky, up at the "U." She is studying agriculture and animal husbandry. She told me that less than two years ago, studies showed that only 0.1% of all cattle killed by predators in wolf restoration areas were actually killed by wolves and only 0.4% of the sheep losses were caused by wolves.   In Minnesota, where wolves reside with livestock, the average loss of livestock to predation by wolves is only 0.03% annually.

I think the "problem" with wolves is being blown all out of proportion. We need to learn how to live with them.

Perspective: Sheep Rancher

The wolves have to go! I am sick and tired of finding dead and bleeding sheep out in my field. I have lost both time and money because some wolf-loving folks from out of state think wolves need to live in this county. Why don't they take the wolves home to live with them?

Just last month, I lost three sheep to wolves. The sheep—one was just a lamb—had teeth marks all over them. The wolves chewed them up a bit and then just left them there to die. They didn't even eat them. They just kill because they enjoy it.

I know you probably don't think I should complain since I was compensated for the loses, but let me tell you, I spent a lot of time and money raising those sheep and the compensation was not enough. And, what about my dog? The wolves killed him, too, and I didn't get any compensation for that. My son was devastated.

If we don't get rid of these wolves, I will have to go out of business. If other ranchers like me go out of business, too, what is going to happen to the economy? No more lamb, no wool. I am sorry, but wolves are just not that important!

ORGANIZE: *Conclusion–Support Notes (C-9)*

- Watch as your teacher models how to complete Conclusion–Support Notes with "Tough Terminator #5, Saltwater Crocodile."

- Now, it is your turn to complete Conclusion–Support Notes based on either the *Tough Terminator* selection or the perspective selection you highlighted. Check with your teacher to find out which.

- Transfer the information you selectively highlighted to the following Conclusion–Support format.

CONCLUSION	SUPPORT

- Compare your Conclusion–Support Notes to those of the other students in your group. Make sure you all agree.

APPLY: *RAFT (D-5)*

- Your teacher will review the RAFT process with you and explain in more detail your RAFT assignment:

    R: A trapper, an animal rights activist, a sheep rancher, a cattle rancher, or the famous author, Sneed B. Collard III
    A: County commissioners at a community meeting
    F: Debate
    T: Convince the commissioners, who will decide the fate of local wolves, that your point of view or solution is the best.

- Debate the wolf issue.

Check Your Understanding

MULTIPLE CHOICE: *(Circle the letter of the correct response.)* With which statement would the author of *Tough Terminators* MOST LIKELY AGREE?
   A. Wolves need to be controlled for safety reasons.
   B. Wolves have changed their habitats over the years.
   C. Wolves are bold and daring.
   D. Wolves are man's best friend.

WRITING ITEM: How do the authors use facts to challenge common misunderstandings about wolves? Use details and information from one of the selections to support your answer.

_____

_____

_____

_____

_____

_____

Continue ➜

_____

_____

REFLECTION

- Talk about how the strategies Selective Highlighting and Underlining, Conclusion–Support Notes, and RAFT helped you understand and remember the information in the selections on the gray wolf.

- What could you have done to be more successful with your learning?

_____

_____

_____

_____

_____

_____

Apply This to Other Classes

- Think about how you can apply these learning strategies to your other classes and record your thoughts below.

_____

_____

_____

_____

_____

_____

- Remember to save samples of successful applications to share with the class and to place in your folder.

Meet the Chapter 17 Strategies "At a Glance"

After completing your CRISS[SM] Learning Plan on the next page, label each of the boxes below with one of the strategies you selected and draw an icon or symbol in each box to represent that strategy. You may add or delete boxes.

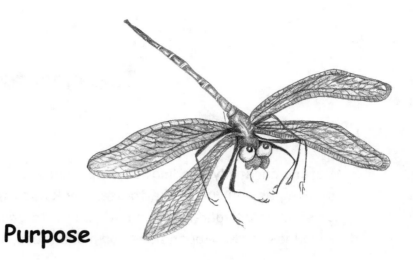

Dragonfly

Purpose

- **Process:** To develop a complete Learning Plan without help from a teacher.

- **Content:** To determine in what ways dragonflies adapt to their environment.

After you have carried out your CRISS^{SM} Learning Plan on the following pages, record, in the box below, the strategies you used.

CRISS^{SM} Learning Plan

Prepare:
Be Involved:
Organize:
Apply:

Implementation

PREPARE: Your Choice

- Before carefully reading the selection with a partner or small group, plan what strategies you would like to use. Look back to earlier chapters to see the types of strategies your teacher had you do to bring out your *background knowledge*. Also look in the Appendices for more ideas.

- Write your plan in the following space.

Before reading, our group plans to... _____

_____

_____

_____

_____

- Use the following space to carry out your plan.

BE INVOLVED: Your Choice

- With a partner or small group, plan what you would like to do while you carefully read the selection. Look back to earlier chapters to see the types of strategies your teacher had you do to keep you *actively involved* with the selection. Also look in the Appendices for more ideas.

- Write your plan in the following space.

_____

_____

_____

_____

_____

- Use the following space to carry out your plan.

<u>ORGANIZE</u>: Your Choice

- With a partner or small group, plan what you would like to do after reading to *organize* and then record the information on the dragonfly in notes. Look back to earlier chapters to see the types of strategies your teacher had you do to help you organize and take notes. Also look in the Appendices for more ideas.

- Write your plan in the following space.

_____

_____

_____

_____

_____

- Use the following space to carry out your plan.

APPLY: Your Choice

- With your partner or small group, plan a strategy that will help you *apply* and learn the information in your dragonfly notes. Look back to earlier chapters to see the types of strategies your teacher had you do to help you apply, use, and learn the information. Also look in the Appendices for more ideas. If you like, you can transform your notes from one organizing structure to another. For example, if you took notes in a Power Map format, you could change them into a Picture Map or into Main Idea—Detail Notes.

- Write your plan in the following space.

_____

_____

_____

_____

_____

- Use the following space to carry out your plan.

Check Your Understanding

MULTIPLE CHOICE: *(Circle the letter of the correct response.)* With which of the following statements would the author MOST LIKELY AGREE?
    A. Dragonflies should be collected and displayed by artists.
    B. Dragonflies are pests and should be eliminated.
    C. Dragonflies help people by eating harmful insects.
    D. Dragonflies are beautiful, but they are not skilled at flying.

WRITING ITEM: According to the author, dragonflies can live in many habitats. What features allow them to survive in these different environments? Use details and information from the selection to support your answer.

_____

_____

_____

_____

_____

_____

_____

REFLECTION

• Talk about how the strategies your group selected helped you understand and remember the information in the selection on the dragonfly.

• What could you have done to be more successful with your learning?

_____

_____

_____

_____

Apply This to Other Classes

- Think about how you can apply the Learning Plan process to your other classes and record your thoughts below.

_____

_____

_____

_____

_____

_____

_____

- Remember to save samples of successful applications to share with the class and to place in your folder.

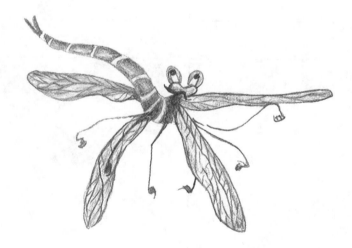

Meet the Chapter 18 Strategies "At a Glance"

After completing your CRISS^{SM} Learning Plan on the next page, label each of the boxes below with one of the strategies you selected and draw an icon or symbol in each box to represent that strategy. You may add or delete boxes.

Gray Whale

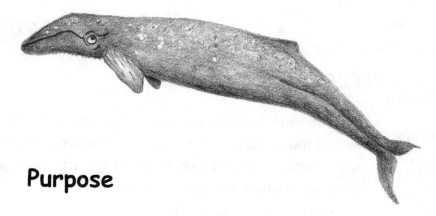

Purpose

- **Process:** To develop a complete Learning Plan without help from a teacher.

- **Content:** To learn how the gray whale can maintain its huge body size.

After you have carried out your CRISS^{SM} Learning Plan on the following pages, record, in the box below, the strategies you used.

CRISS^{SM} Learning Plan

Prepare:
Be Involved:
Organize:
Apply:

Implementation

PREPARE: *Your Choice*

- By yourself, before you carefully read the selection, plan what strategies you would like to use. Look back to earlier chapters to see the types of strategies your teacher had you do to bring out your *background knowledge*. Also look in the Appendices for more ideas.

- Write your plan in the following space.

_____

_____

_____

_____

_____

- Use the following space to carry out your plan.

BE INVOLVED: *Your Choice*

- By yourself, plan what you would like to do while you carefully read the selection. Look back to earlier chapters to see the types of strategies your teacher had you do to keep you *actively involved* with the selection. Also look in the Appendices for more ideas.

- Write your plan in the following space.

_____

_____

_____

_____

_____

- Use the following space to carry out your plan.

<u>ORGANIZE</u>: *Your Choice*

- By yourself, plan what you would like to do after reading to *organize* and then record the information on the gray whale in notes. Look back to earlier chapters to see the types of strategies your teacher had you do to help you organize and take notes. Also look in the Appendices for more ideas.

- Write your plan in the following space.

_____

_____

_____

_____

_____

- Use the following space to carry out your plan.

APPLY: *Your Choice*

- By yourself, select a strategy that will help you *apply* and learn the information in your gray whale notes. Look back to earlier chapters to see the types of strategies your teacher had you do to help you apply, use, and learn the information. Also look in the Appendices for more ideas. Remember, you may transform your notes from one organizing structure to another. For example, if you took notes in a Picture Map format, you could transfer them into Main Idea-Detail Notes, or you could compare the information in your notes to notes you took on other animals and use a Venn Diagram or a Content Frame.

- Write your plan in the following space.

_____

_____

_____

_____

_____

- Use the following space to carry out your plan.

Check Your Understanding

MULTIPLE CHOICE: *(Circle the letter of the correct response.)* Based on the information in the article, what is the BEST PREDICTION of what will happen next?
- A. Gray whales will continue to increase in numbers.
- B. Gray whales will decline in numbers.
- C. Gray whales will need new laws to protect them.
- D. Gray whales will disappear as a result of man hunting them.

WRITING ITEM: What does the gray whale do to earn his reputation as "the world's biggest vacuum"? Use details and information from the selection to support your answer.

_____

_____

_____

_____

_____

_____

_____

_____

REFLECTION
- Talk about how the strategies you selected helped you understand and remember the information in the selection on the gray whale.

- What could you have done to be more successful with your learning?

_____

_____

_____

_____

_____

Apply This to Other Classes

- Now that you have developed a Learning Plan all by yourself on the gray whale, write out a plan below based on a specific reading selection from one of your other classes.

Class: _____

Reading Selection: _____

Prepare: _____

_____

Be Involved: _____

_____

Organize: _____

_____

Apply: _____

_____

- Remember to save all of your work from the above lesson plan to share with the class and to place in your folder.

Meet the Chapter 19 Strategies "At a Glance"

RECIPROCAL TEACHING

❖ SUMMARIZE.

❖ QUESTION.

❖ NOTE DIFFICULT PARTS.

❖ PREDICT.

PROBLEM-SOLUTION

Problem:

Effects:

Causes:

Solutions:

CONCLUSION-SUPPORT NOTES

Conclusion	Support
Predators are **helpful** to humans.	• By eating pests, they prevent the spread of diseases & help production of crops.
Predators are **harmful** to humans.	• They compete with people for food.

The Top Predator

Purpose

- **Process:** To become familiar with the strategies of Reciprocal Teaching, Problem–Solution Notes, Conclusion–Support Notes, and Persuasive Paragraph Writing and to be able to apply these strategies in other classes.

- **Content:** To identify why the author thinks people are the most important predator of all.

CRISS^SM Learning Plan

Prepare:	*Two-Column Notes (+ and –)*
Be Involved:	*Reciprocal Teaching*
Organize:	*Problem–Solution Notes*
Apply:	*Conclusion–Support Notes, Persuasive Paragraph Writing*

Implementation

PREPARE: *Two-Column Notes (+ and –)*

- Turn to pages 4 and 5 in your *Tough Terminators* book. As you listen to your teacher or a classmate read "About Predators" think about all of the predators you have studied this year. In the space below, write the name of the animal you think might be labeled the "Top Predator." Your selection may be one of the twelve you have studied or another animal with which you are familiar.

I think the top predator is probably _____ .

- Now, your teacher is going to read the last paragraphs of the terminator selections. See if you change your mind after hearing these paragraphs.

- What do you know about the interaction of man and other animals? Your teacher is going to fill in a "+ and –" Two-Column Chart with your help.

BE INVOLVED: *Reciprocal Teaching (B-5)*

- Your teacher will explain and model for you how to do Reciprocal Teaching with the first paragraph or two of "The Top Predator."

- Complete "The Top Predator" selection with a partner. Silently read the next paragraph, then one of you will do the four parts of Reciprocal Teaching: summarizing, questioning, noting difficult parts, and predicting what will come next. Switch roles with each paragraph until you have completed the selection.

ORGANIZE: *Problem–Solution Notes (C-10)*

- Watch as your teacher models how to record information in a Problem–Solution format.

- Use the following Problem–Solution format to record your notes from the "Top Predator" selection. You may include information from other parts of the *Tough Terminator* book as well. The problem you will clarify is: " 'People predators' who have a negative impact on the earth and its creatures."

PROBLEM–SOLUTION NOTES

Problem/Issue:	*"People predators" who have a negative impact on the earth and its creatures.*
Effects:	
Causes:	
Solutions/ resolutions:	

APPLY: *Conclusion–Support Notes (C-9) and Persuasive Paragraph*

- Select the best solution from your Problem–Solution Notes. In the left column of the Conclusion–Support format on the next page, write a sentence which states you think *that solution* is the best solution to the problem: *"'People predators' who have a negative impact on the earth and its creatures."*

- In the right-hand column, "support" your conclusion with at least three reasons why you think your solution will work best. Remember, you may use information from any part of the *Tough Terminators* book.

CONCLUSION	SUPPORT
1	2.
	2.
	2.

Write your paragraph here:

- Now, write a Persuasive Paragraph in the bottom box of the Conclusion–Support form, to convince an audience that the solution you selected is the best.

Check Your Understanding

MULTIPLE CHOICE: *(Circle the letter of the correct response.)* With which of the following statements below would the author of this book MOST LIKELY DISAGREE?

    A. Being predators has helped humans survive.

    B. Human activities affect the earth and its creatures.

    C. By keeping a pond in the back yard or avoiding spraying pesticides in the back yard, people can help small predators such as the ladybird beetle and the dragonfly.

    D. Over-fishing helps food sources in many areas.

WRITING ITEM: According to the author, "[people] are the most important predators of all." Use details from the selection to support this conclusion.

_____

_____

_____

_____

_____

_____

_____

EXTENDED RESPONSE: Reflect upon all of the predators you have learned about in this book. If you could choose to be one of them, which one would it be? Use details and information about this animal to explain your choice.

_____

_____

_____

_____

_____

Continue ➥

_____

_____

_____

_____

_____

REFLECTION

- Talk about how the strategies Reciprocal Teaching, Problem–Solution Notes, Conclusion–Support Notes, and Persuasive Paragraph Writing helped you understand and remember the information in the selection on "The Top Predator."

- What could you have done to be more successful with your learning?

_____

_____

_____

_____

Apply This to Other Classes

- Think about how you can apply these learning strategies to your other classes and record your thoughts below.

_____

_____

_____

_____

- Remember to save samples of successful applications to share with the class and to place in your folder.

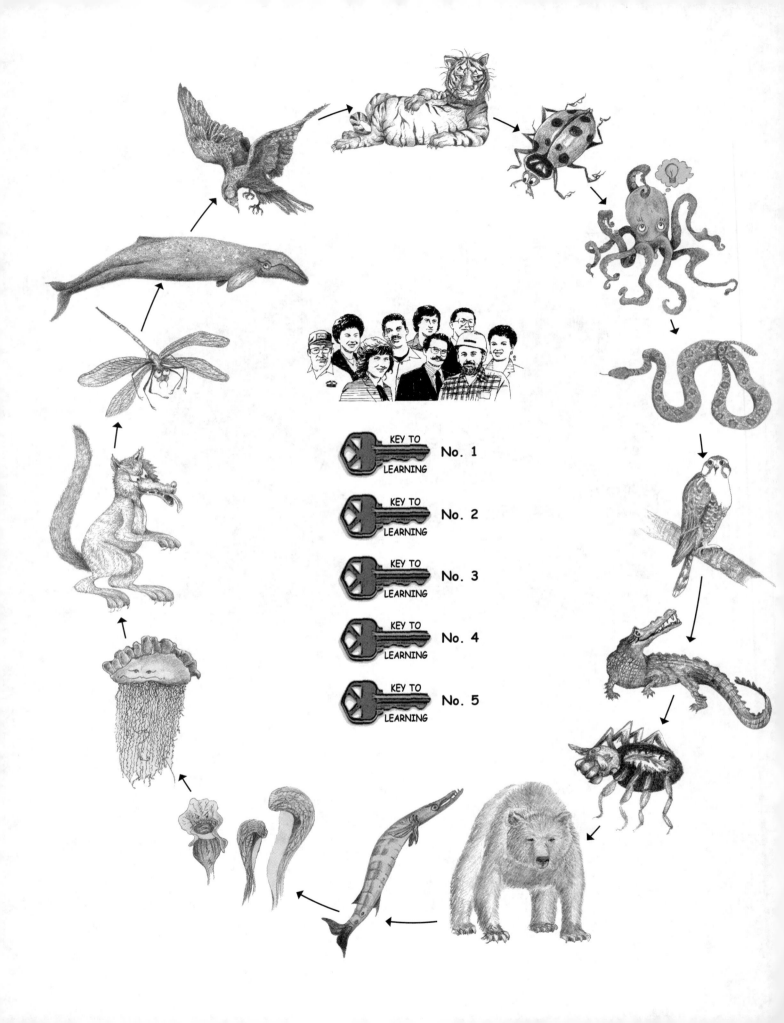

KEY TO LEARNING — No. 1

KEY TO LEARNING — No. 2

KEY TO LEARNING — No. 3

KEY TO LEARNING — No. 4

KEY TO LEARNING — No. 5

APPENDICES

Strategies Reference

CRISS℠ LEARNING PLAN

A-1

To have success with your reading, viewing, and listening, you need to:

PREPARE *by thinking about what you already know and by setting purposes.*

BE INVOLVED *as you read, view, and/or listen. Think about the information, make connections, monitor your understanding.*

ORGANIZE the information by transforming it in a new way, i.e., use different words, draw pictures, create a map.

APPLY *what you have learned to solve problems, to make connections, and to apply the information to new situations.*

KEYS TO LEARNING

A-2

1. AUTHOR'S CRAFT

2. BACKGROUND KNOWLEDGE

3. PURPOSE SETTING

4. ACTIVE LEARNING

5. METACOGNITION

To make the keys work, remember to:

1. WRITE

2. DISCUSS

3. ORGANIZE

K - W - L
P L U S

A-3

K: What do you *K*now?

W: What do you *W*ant to learn?

L: What did you *L*earn?

Plus: Organize the information
Power notes, maps, frames,
2-column notes, etc.

Plus: Practice the information
summarize, discuss, draw,
apply, etc.

PATTERN PUZZLE

A-4

1. Make a copy of your notes, a section of text, a mathematics or science process, the events in a story, etc.

2. Cut the copy into sentences, steps, or events.

3. Mix up the pieces.

4. Learn the information or process by putting the pieces in the correct order.

5. Compare your solution to the original.

6. Try again!

POWER THINKING

A-5

Power 1: Main idea

Power 2: A detail or support of a Power 1

Power 3: A detail or support of a Power 2

Power 4: A detail or support of a Power 3

1. Food
   2. Junk food
      3. Chips
   2. Healthy food
      3. Vegetables
         4. Carrots
      3. Fruit

SELECTIVE HIGHLIGHTING & UNDERLINING

A-6

- Know your purpose
- Read a paragraph before marking
- Re-read to highlight or underline
- Remember these guidelines:

  – *Be selective*
  (mark key words, not sentences)

  – *Use symbols * ! ? > →*

  – *Add Power numbers*

  – *Write in the margins*

AUTHENTIC QUESTIONS

B-1

Type of Question	Question Starters
Recall	who, what, list, repeat, identify, name, when, define
Analysis	summarize, divide, categorize, separate
Comparison	compare, contrast
Inference	predict, conclude, what if, anticipate
Evaluation	judge, defend, prove, assess

MIND STREAMING

B-2

1. Work with a partner.

2. Determine a topic.

3. Tell your partner everything you know about the topic for one minute.

4. Your partner only listens (no talking!).

5. Reverse roles.

6. Your partner tells everything she knows for one minute.

7. Write down agreed upon information.

QUESTION–ANSWER RELATIONSHIPS
(QARs)

B-3

In the Book QARs

- *Right There:*
  The answer is in the text in one sentence.

- *Think and Search:*
  The answer is in the text in several places.

In My Head QARs

- *Author and You:*
  Put together what the author says
  and what you know.

- *On My Own:*
  The answer relates to the text, but you
  use your ideas, not the author's.

READ-AND-SAY-SOMETHING

B-4

1. Work with a partner or small group.

2. Read one paragraph or section of text at a time (silently or out loud).

3. Make a comment or ask a question about the information.

4. Your partner or other group members add their comments and questions.

5. When discussion stops, read another paragraph or section.

6. Let a different group member start the discussion.

RECIPROCAL TEACHING

B-5

One student at a time follows the procedure below until the entire selection has been completed.

- Read through one paragraph or short section of text.

- **Summarize** what it means.

- Develop a **question** or two over the content.

- **Note** any difficult vocabulary and predict what the words might mean.

- **Predict** what you think will happen next.

SEED DISCUSSIONS

B-6

"Seeds" grow into great discussions!

Here are some possible seeds:
- *Questions about characters, events, or information*

- *Descriptive writing that you particularly enjoy*

- *Events or information which remind you of things you know*

- *Things which seem interesting or surprising*

STICKY-NOTE DISCUSSIONS

B-7

Read a selection and mark key parts with sticky notes.

Here are some things you can mark:

- *What you don't understand*

- *What makes you sad, mad, happy, frustrated, etc.*

- *Support for your opinion*

- *Places to add your own pictures or examples*

Remember:

- *Write explanations on the sticky notes*

- *Discuss with a partner or group*

THINK – PAIR – SHARE

B-8

- **Select** *a topic.*

- **Think** *about the topic and write down what you know.*

- **Pair** *with another student to check your ideas.*

- **Share** *your ideas with the whole class.*

CONTENT FRAMES

C-1

Categories on the left
Subdivisions across the top

Example

Spiders	Physical Appearance	Habitat	Food	Life Cycle	Predators
Black Widow					
Tarantula					
Orchard Spider					

Carefully read the text to fill in the blank squares.

CONTRAST and COMPARE GUIDE

C-2

(SUBJECT 1)	(SUBJECT 2)

↙ HOW DIFFERENT? ↘

With regard to . . .

1   2

↘ HOW SIMILAR? ↙

With regard to . . .   1 & 2

Conclusion:

GRAPHIC
ORGANIZERS 1

C-3

Power Map

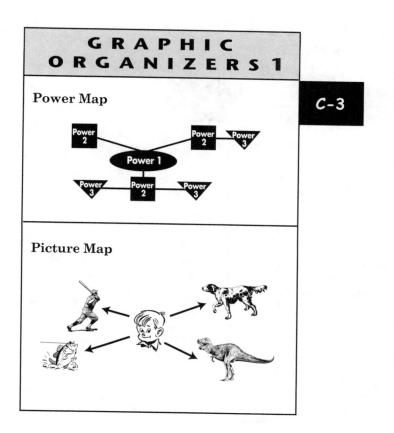

Picture Map

GRAPHIC
ORGANIZERS 2

C-4

Sequence Map

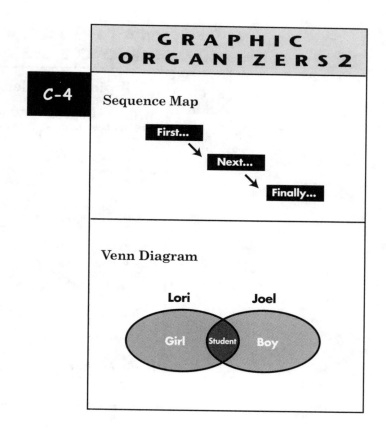

Venn Diagram

MATH ORGANIZER 1
PROBLEM SOLVING
GUIDE

C-5

1. QUESTION

2. MATHEMATICAL PLAN

3. PROBLEM SOLVING PLAN (Pre-writing)

4. WRITTEN ANSWER plus the process used to determine the answer. [Start by changing the question in box 1 to a statement.]

5. CHECK YOUR ANSWER
   Does your answer make sense?

MATH ORGANIZER 2
PROCESS NOTES

C-6

Topic or Problem: $\frac{1}{2} + \frac{2}{3}$

Write the steps of the process here.	Work through an example here.
Find a common denominator	1) $2 \times 3 = 6$
Rewrite over the common denominator	2) $\frac{1}{2} = \frac{3}{6}$ $\frac{2}{3} = \frac{4}{6}$
Add the top numbers, keep bottom the same	3) $\frac{3}{6} + \frac{4}{6} = \frac{7}{6}$
Reduce	4) Can't
Change to a mixed number	5) $1\frac{1}{6}$

TWO-COLUMN NOTES 1
MAIN IDEA–
DETAIL NOTES

C-7

1. Topic

Main Ideas	Details
2.	3.
	3.
	4.
2.	3.

1. Next Topic

2.	3.
	4.
	4.

C: ORGANIZING

TWO-COLUMN NOTES 2
STORY PLAN

C-8

Title of Story or Event	
Setting	Time and place
Characters	Who are the most important people?
Problem	What problem does the main character have?
Goal	What does the main character hope to accomplish?
Events	List the main events in the story.
Resolution	How does it end?

TWO-COLUMN NOTES 3
CONCLUSION - SUPPORT NOTES

C-9

1. (Conclusion)	2. (Support) 3. (Why)
1. I love chocolate!	2. The taste 3. It is creamy and sweet and makes me feel good.

TWO-COLUMN NOTES 4
PROBLEM - SOLUTION NOTES

C-10

Topic: Finances

What is the *Problem?*	*Not enough allowance*
What are the *Effects?*	• *Can't buy clothes and/or video games* • *Can't go to movies* • *Feel badly*
What are the *Causes?*	• *Parents can't afford higher allowance* • *I don't help around the house*
What are the *Solutions?*	• *Get a job* • *Help out more*

LEARNING LOG ENTRIES 1

D-1

Free Response: *Anything goes! Write questions or comments, or draw pictures.*

Dialogue: *Write to a classmate or to your teacher.*

Pre- and Post-reading: *Write before you read and tell what you already know. After reading, make corrections and add new information.*

Observation: *(great for labs and field trips) Write what you see, hear, smell, taste, and/or feel. Develop questions and make predictions.*

LEARNING LOG ENTRIES 2

D-2

Perspective: *Write your entry as if you were a person or thing in the story.*

Process: *Write out the steps in a process or the steps to solve a problem.*

Explanation: *Explain how and/or why something functions.*

Literary elements: *(Use with fiction.) Write about...*
> *the main character.*
> *the setting.*
> *the characters' problems.*
> *your favorite quotes.*
> *descriptive language.*

D: WRITING

ONE-SENTENCE SUMMARIES

D-3

Description
  A _____ is a kind of_____that . . . .

Compare / Contrast
  __x__ and __y__ are similar in that they both . . . , but__x__ . . . , while__y__ . . . .

Sequence
  _____begins with . . . , continues with . . . , and ends with . . . .

Problem / Solution
  _____wanted . . . , but . . . , so . . . .

Cause / Effect
  _____happens because . . . .
  _____causes . . . .

D: WRITING

POWER WRITING

D-4

The Power 1 sentence tells the number of Power 2s.

  Examples
  I learned two things in class yesterday.

  Exercise improves my health in three ways.

Use active verbs.
  Don't use "is," "was," "are," etc.

Complete paragraphs usually have a form similar to:
    1, 2, 2, 2, 1
    1, 2, 3, 2, 3, 1

RAFT

D-5

R: **R**ole of the writer
Who or what are you?

A: **A**udience
To whom are you writing?

F: **F**ormat of the work
letter, poem, song, picture, video, etc.

T: **T**opic with a strong verb
urge, warn, plead, honor, attack, etc.

SPOOL PAPER

D-6

Introduction: Starts with a "grabber" (Power 0) and ends with a thesis or Power 1 sentence.

Body: Expands on the Power 2 ideas in the thesis - it contains at least two paragraphs.

Conclusion: Starts with a restatement of the thesis (1) followed by the "clincher" (0) or wrap-up.

D: WRITING

SUMMARIZING

D-7

- **Read** *the entire selection.*

- **List** *the important ideas you remember.*

- **Re-read** *to check and add to your list.*

- **Group** *similar ideas together.*

- **Delete** *less important ideas.*

- **Arrange** *in Power notes or a Power map.*

- **Write** *a summary from your notes.*

D: WRITING

WRITING TEMPLATES

D-8

1. Organize your information in Two-Column Notes or a map.

2. Write a main idea statement or Power 1 sentence

3. Add a signal word for each support or detail
   - ✎ *First, next*
   - ✎ *For example, in addition*

4. Use one more signal word for your concluding sentence
   - ✎ *In conclusion*
   - ✎ *Finally*

5. Fill in the template with the information in your notes/map.

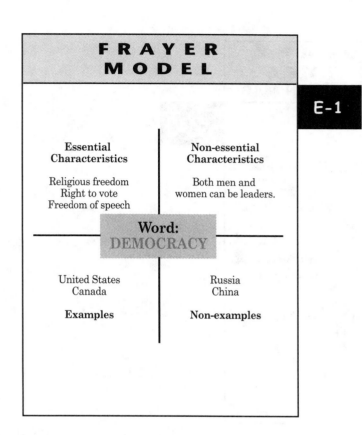

FRAYER MODEL

E-1

Essential Characteristics	Non-essential Characteristics
Religious freedom Right to vote Freedom of speech	Both men and women can be leaders.

Word: DEMOCRACY

United States Canada	Russia China
Examples	**Non-examples**

SENTENCE AND WORD EXPANSION

E-2

By brainstorming, expansion can help you elaborate on concepts.

Original Sentence:
> The dog went to the house.

> dog: well-fed scotty, newly-coifed poodle
> went: arrogantly tiptoed, tripped awkwardly
> house: gaudy mansion, adobe, shady cabin

New Sentence:
> The newly-coifed poodle arrogantly tiptoed up the front steps of the gaudy mansion.

Expansion is also used for worn-out words:

"Said"– replace with: exclaimed, whispered, cried, yelled, whined, murmured, grumbled, gasped, etc.

VOCABULARY MAPPING TYPE 1
CONCEPT OF DEFINITION MAP

E-3

Type 1:

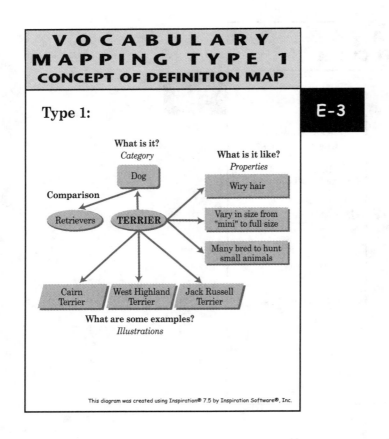

What is it?
Category

Dog

Comparison

Retrievers   TERRIER

What is it like?
Properties

Wiry hair

Vary in size from "mini" to full size

Many bred to hunt small animals

Cairn Terrier   West Highland Terrier   Jack Russell Terrier

What are some examples?
Illustrations

This diagram was created using Inspiration® 7.5 by Inspiration Software®, Inc.

VOCABULARY MAPPING TYPE 2
WORD MAP

E-4

Type 2:

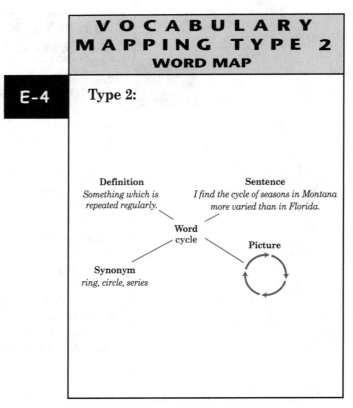

Definition
Something which is repeated regularly.

Sentence
I find the cycle of seasons in Montana more varied than in Florida.

Word
cycle

Picture

Synonym
ring, circle, series

VOCABULARY FLASH CARDS

E-5

Side 1: Illustration
Word divided into syllables

TRADITIONAL IDEAS

i • con • o • clast

Side 2: Definition
Synonym & antonym
Original sentence

iconoclast

Definition: a person who attacks popular ideas or traditions
(sometimes religious ideas)

Synonym: attacker, overthrower, rebel

Antonym: follower, conformist, brown-noser

Sentence: We feared the iconoclast might be elected to an important
state office and eliminate the programs in which we all believe.

WORD COMBINING

E-6

Combine three to five related
vocabulary terms into one or
two sentences.

Words:
circle, center, radius, diameter

Sentence:
The _diameter_ of a _circle_, which
is twice the length of the circle's
radius, is the distance across the
circle and through its _center_.

E: VOCABULARY

INDEX

NOTES

NOTES